ALBERT EINSTEIN

ALBERT EINSTEIN

The Man and His Theories

by Hilaire Cuny

TRANSLATED BY MERVYN SAVILL

A Profile in Science

PAUL S. ERIKSSON, INC.
New York

For Eliane, and as a tribute to
Prince Louis de Broglie

Contents

		PAGE
1	Albert Einstein, the Man	11
2	The First Works of Einstein	21
3	The Life of Einstein	59
4	The General Theory of Relativity	69
5	Einstein the Fighter and the Persecuted	93
6	The Last Years	105

Choice of Texts

(a)	A few of Albert Einstein's reflections	115
(b)	Einstein's Ethics and Outlook	123
(c)	Physics and Reality	129
	I. General considerations concerning scientific method. Stratification of the scientific system	129
	II. Mechanics and the attempts to base the whole of physics on this discipline	134
	III. The conception of the field	142
	IV. The theory of relativity	145
(d)	Einstein and the Idea of Freedom	153
(e)	Against what Einstein called "International Anarchy"	157
(f)	A few of Albert Einstein's Opinions	161
	Glossary of scientific terms	165
	Bibliography	169
	Index	173

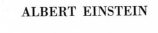

ALBERT EINSTEIN

1

---

*Albert Einstein, the Man**

ALBERT EINSTEIN, the most famous scientist of the twentieth century, perhaps the greatest genius of all time, whose titles to fame are uncontested, was a man of touching simplicity. It was no pose and still less was it ingenuousness, but he was always surprised by the masses' infatuation with his theories, because they could not possibly mean anything to them. Those who understood or could understand him did not crowd around him like primitives at the feet of their idol. They read, criticized, and discussed him.

He did not care for honors, but no man has ever had so many honors, titles, and decorations conferred upon him. He did not protest, but merely ignored them. For him they were entirely meaningless.

Einstein did nothing "to achieve glory," nothing for money, nothing to outclass others, and certainly nothing "to please people." He strove to disentangle the laws of the universe, as an amateur and dilettante, but he was a prodigious thinker and a worker whom success importuned. He wanted quite simply to be a man who brought his grain of sand to the common fund: in actual fact he presented the world with a diamond mine.

"One should," he said, "guard against inculcating a young man with the idea that success is the aim of life, for a success-

* A glossary of technical terms for the benefit of the lay reader is given at the end of this work.

11

ful man normally receives from his peers an incomparably greater portion than the services he has been able to render them deserve. The value of a man resides in what he gives and not in what he is capable of receiving. The most important motive for study at school, at the university, and in life is the pleasure of working and of thereby obtaining results which will serve the community. The most important task for our educators is to awaken and encourage these psychological forces in a young man. Such a basis alone can lead to the joy of possessing one of the most precious assets in the world—knowledge or artistic skill."

To succeed, in fact, does not mean having talent; it does not signify "to know"; even less does it imply genius. Those who impose themselves are not necessarily the best, for the latter are fully aware what an illusory thing is fame; they are not always the most intelligent or above all the most worthy and of the greatest integrity. More often than one might imagine the most important posts are filled by brilliant nonentities, with superior conditioning, that is to say educated and cultivated, but incapable of creating something new or facing up to new situations.

Einstein never wore any medals, not even the most discreet ribbon. For a long time he refused to buy himself an evening suit because he considered it made him look ridiculous. With regard to clothes he preferred a pair of old baggy trousers and a woolen pullover. He often went barefoot or in sandals, not as an affectation but because quite genuinely it made him feel at ease and relaxed.

Urbane in the extreme toward the modest, he was barely civil to the great ones of the world, or those classified as such. He knew how to reply with a categorical "No" to boring invitations, to eject "lion hunters," and to resist deceptive seductions.

He had no respect at all for money and absolutely none for finance. Moreover, he considered money as one of the greatest of human ills. Discoursing one day with Charlie Chaplin, who was explaining his theory of the gold standard, Einstein said that if it rested with him all the world currencies, shares, and bonds would be heaped on an enormous bonfire around which the crowds would celebrate their liberation from an age-old tyranny.

His basic good will caused Antonina Vallentin, who had the

rare privilege of being one of his intimates, to write: "His kindness radiates like a light that is indifferent to what it illuminates. But this kindness is not that of the great seducers whose need to please is their very breath of life. It is an expression of his fundamental balance just as his gaiety is a manifestation of his moral health. His good will originates from a sense of social justice for which he himself admits that he is impassioned. His compassion for the victims of persecution, for those who are crushed by poverty, is not the reaction of an acute sensitivity, a shudder at the sight of suffering. He never feels the embarrassment of a healthy man confronted by an invalid, nor that vague guilty conscience which sometimes overcomes people when faced with undeserved misfortune. It is rather a sense of responsibility which immediately preoccupies him."

Einstein's personality was a study in light and shade. Affable with everyone except with the pretentious, he hated to commit himself. Professor Franck, his colleague and friend, stresses his reticence in entering into intimate personal relationships. "This trait in his character," he wrote, "always made him a lone wolf among his students, colleagues, friends, and even his family." But this attitude of apparent negation was due above all to the little interest he took in the problems of material life, in those trifles which for the vast majority of men and women, and even for those who may be dearest to us, remain almost the sole topic of conversation.

"This dislike of vapid talk," says Franck, "was more than compensated by a boundless urge to discuss scientific problems and questions of general interest with his colleagues. Without the least ostentation he ran to them for advice, and even to people much younger than himself if they were in closer touch with certain problems. All this incidentally with perfect simplicity."

Einstein's attitude toward others and his behavior in life were certainly not contrived. He did not create his own legend as so many others believe that they should do. When asked to give a portrait of himself toward the end of his life he wrote quite simply: "Of what is significant in one's own existence one is hardly aware, and it certainly should not bother the other fellow. What does a fish know about the water in which he swims all his life?

"The bitter and the sweet come from the outside, the hard

from within, from one's own efforts. For the most part I do the thing which my own nature drives me to do. It is embarrassing to earn so much respect and love for it. Arrows of hate have been shot at me too; but they never hit me, because somehow they belonged to another world, with which I have no connection whatsoever."

From the physical point of view this is how a woman, again Antonina Vallentin, saw the man: "You had to see Einstein in a small skiff to be able to judge the strength of the roots which attached him to a primitive life. Barefoot or in sandals, his white ducks baggy at the knees, sagging at the hips, his broad chest molded in an old pullover or a faded swimming suit, his powerful neck bare, reddened by sun and wind, his leonine head with its aura of long hair standing on end, he stood swaying gently to the rocking of the boat as though nailed to the deck and at one with the sail he maneuvered. . . . The low horizon enlarged him out of proportion. The sun beat down on his screwed-up eyes, his face grimaced under the biting of the wind, his hair was tousled and the muscles of his arms were knotted like cords. He tugged at the sail, shouted something at me, and his mouth formed an O. The wind carried away his words. He looked so pagan, so healthily animal, that he seemed to have loomed up from the heart of the elements, from the age of the sea gods or pirates. In fact he looked anything else than a scientist."

THE YOUTH OF ALBERT EINSTEIN

Albert Einstein was born on March 14, 1879, at Ulm in the province of Württemberg. His father, Hermann, owned a small electrochemical concern which he transferred to Munich the following year.

Hermann Einstein was no scientist. He was what is known as a *bon vivant*. On Sundays he liked to go on trips to the outskirts of Munich among the foothills or by the lakeside, stopping at the inns with their welcoming tables, where the family found plenty of beer, excellent sausages, and crisp radishes.

Jewish by origin, religion left Hermann cold, and certainly neither little Albert nor his sister Maya were ever conditioned by their father's religion. In common with most Germans of the period, Hermann Einstein admired Bismarck and William I, while chafing at the Prussian hegemony: strange duality in this "romantic" who enthused over Schiller and Heine. . . . But did not most of his compatriots at the time possess this type of mind, whereas the French thought of nothing but revenge?

In the streets of the Munich of Albert Einstein's youth, the children's great distraction was to follow the soldiers on parade, carried away like the grownups by the brass and the drums. Albert, who at school always avoided his schoolmates, who did not join them in their games of playing soldiers, who did not care for running, jumping, or any other violent exercise, wandered off one day, deep in thought, from one of these manifestations. A passerby, misinterpreting the reason for his melancholy, reproached him gaily:

"Cheer up, my boy. You'll soon be old enough to march like those fine soldiers."

"Old enough?" he replied in surprise. "But I was just thinking, sir, that I should not like to be a soldier and become a machine."

Albert Einstein was never a good pupil. His marks were mediocre, and he never reached the top of his class. At one moment his family even thought that he was retarded. He did not talk until the age of three. His behavior as a schoolboy left so much to be desired that his mother wrote to a woman friend: "I don't know what we're going to do with Albert, he doesn't seem to learn very much."

Oddly enough, what attracted him, apart from mathematics for which he seemed to have a natural gift, was religious instruction. Hermann, the far from orthodox Jew, had sent him to a Catholic institution (in Germany at that time there were only Lutheran schools), where he acquired a great interest in "divinity," the biblical legends, and the epic of Christ. In this subject he often surpassed his fellow pupils, although he was the only Jew among them. Philipp Franck writes: "A characteristic feature of Einstein's religious sentiment as a child was that he saw no great difference between what he learned of Catholicism at school and the vague remains of the Jewish tradition with which he was familiar at home. All this made him feel that the universe obeyed certain laws, that this harmony was represented by various categories of symbols which he judged more from their aesthetic value than as symbols of the 'truth.' "

Little Albert had a constitutional horror of lies. He did not like uttering conventional phrases. In derision he was nicknamed *Biedermeier*—it means roughly "Honest John"—to such an extent did this honesty, which made him hesitate to reply to a question until he had thought it over for a long time, seem to be an anomaly if not a grave defect.

At the age of ten he left primary school for the Luitpold Gymnasium in Munich, where he showed no more brilliance than at primary school. He considered it stupid to learn things by heart. The rigorous discipline which was a feature of education in Germany oppressed him so much that even as an adult he retained a feeling of resentment for his teachers. Of schoolmasters, he said that they "appeared to him as sergeants" and of professors that they behaved "like lieutenants." Throughout his life he despised the military, their brutal manners, stereotyped behavior, their abuse of authority toward those whom they considered to be "inferiors," their obsequiousness toward "superiors," and their automatic obedience to the Establishment.

It was thanks to books of popular science that Albert Einstein felt a passion for knowledge awaken in him. He wanted to know everything about the mysteries of the universe. His favorite classic writers were Schiller and Goethe. At a very early age his mother had made him take violin lessons, and gradually his rather mild enthusiasm was transformed into a passion for music. Doubtless he was not a virtuoso as some people have tried to maintain, but he could hold his own very respectably among amateurs.

A love of music is often to be found among great mathematicians. They undoubtedly have an innate receptivity to musical waves—one has only to recall child prodigies such as Mozart. It would seem that there exists a special attuning of the integrating cortical structures of musicians closely connected with the faculty for the assimilation of numbers. I mean that an inborn facility for mathematics is often accompanied by a talent for music, to cite, for example, fabulous calculators such as Inaudi.

Intelligence has nothing to do with it. Brilliant calculators (I do not say mathematicians because there is a great gulf between the two) have often been uncultivated people of very moderate intelligence. There are also brilliant noncreative mathematicians, whose intelligence, taken in the broadest sense—particularly within the framework of analysis and above all of synthesis—remains average. Einstein possessed all these gifts, and this is why he was a genius. Mathematics is in actual fact the most advanced form of abstraction. A volume needed to explain a physical phenomenon can be reduced to a few formulae which seem complicated to us merely because we are not mathematicians. But the higher mathematician deciphers these formulae with ease, and for him they are the sole reality: our own representations always surprise him. For example, having never had the benefits of a sound mathematical education, I had to work very hard to understand various relativity equations, and even now I am not wholly satisfied. I need to translate them into "the concrete." For the mathematician this translation is unnecessary; a mere glance at the formula is enough. It is as clear to him as a very ordinary word is to us. A word is in fact an abstraction. When for example we use a word such as "cat," we see the animal in question before our eyes (or rather we evoke it in our mind's eye). Incidentally, this image will be very different according to the individual and according to his degree of cultivation. It is obvious that for the average person the word "cat" evokes only the morphological image of the animal (its head, paws, ears, fur and tail). In the case of a naturalist, the representation born of the abstraction "cat" develops considerably and the image becomes incredibly complex. Not only does he imagine "a single cat" or even "a single species of cats," but the whole family of felines, not only externally (morphologically) but also internally (physico-anatomically). Should the naturalist happen to be an animal psychologist, his mental field of action is again enlarged. Thus according to our knowledge we can pronounce a few phrases or write a whole book by the mere evocation of a single word.

Conversely, a very primitive language, in other words a language with a limited number of words in which, for example, the single word "animal" would identify the whole species, would demand a host of explanations in conversation before it could be understood precisely which animal was being discussed. Herein lies the whole value of language and of its corollary, writing; its potential for abstraction is transcended by mathematics thanks to symbols which can be understood in any country. Mathematics is a universal language.

It remains to be known whether every mathematician "sees" reality. Einstein obviously had this power, and we shall return to the subject later. This commentary merely serves to stress, apart from the importance of the mathematical concept, that everything seems to take place as though it existed in the realm of mathematics as in that of music, a psychic terrain favorable to the development of these qualities. Thus although he was not particularly "good at book-learning," the pupil Einstein clearly outclassed his school fellows in the domain of mathematics.

When he was fifteen years old, his father became involved in financial difficulties and was obliged to give up his business in Munich and leave his homeland for Italy to try to start one of the same nature in Milan.

Albert would have preferred to have gone with the family, but Hermann decided that his son should continue his studies at the *lycée* in order to get a diploma which would open the doors of the university to him, a university degree being indispensable for obtaining a good situation and for the choice of a liberal profession. This was his ambition.

Albert Einstein therefore remained in Munich on his own in a "private boarding house." Here he was subject to restraint as at college. He did not like discipline, in fact he never liked or tolerated it. He felt an alien in this hostile milieu. Despising coarseness, incapable of automatic gestures, with little talent for the physical exercises favored by his comrades, he began to cause mutual embarrassment between the young people of his age and also between the professors and himself. This could not continue. Actually it lasted only six months. He did everything in his power to leave the Gymnasium. He wanted to see Italy, which his father imprudently described in his letters as a dream country, particularly with regard to the mentality so different from the Prussian spirit that ruled human behavior with an iron rod.

Mathematics proved an unexpected ally. His professor in this discipline gave him a certificate to say that his extraordinary capacities would give him immediate entrée to any institution where "maths" was the major subject. Student status, he knew, was less rigid abroad than in Germany, and possibly Albert could win diplomas there more easily. Besides, they were not particularly anxious to keep this troublemaker to whom they had often been obliged to say: "Your presence in this class ruins the respect of the students."

So at last Albert Einstein was in Milan. His first gesture was to abandon German nationality and at the same time to turn his back on all religious sects. To be a stateless person and an atheist was scandalous in those days.

He found life in Italy very pleasant, but he had to think about "making a career." Hermann, more and more involved in his financial difficulties, urged him to finish his studies, which he could only do in a German-speaking institution. He himself had retired from the German community. One solution remained: Switzerland.

The most famous technological establishment at the period in the Swiss Federation—and even in Central Europe, outside Germany—was the Zürich Polytechnic. Albert was naturally attracted toward this institution, but his weakness in subjects other than mathematics was an obstacle. He failed the entrance examination. Nevertheless, the director of the "Poly," on the strength of his exceptional powers in mathematics, encouraged him not to despair and advised him to take a preparatory course in the excellent Cantonal Gymnasium at Aarau. This would exempt him from taking the university entrance exam again.

Albert found Aarau a pleasant change from German educatory methods. Here there was no military training, but an effective collaboration between professors and pupils; at the end of the school year he had profited so well from his courses that he was able to enter the Polytechnic, where he was to complete his studies with great brilliance.

His adult life began at the turn of the century.

A MINOR CIVIL SERVANT

Albert Einstein, the exceptional scholar, came up against a wall of refusals when he tried to obtain a post as assistant on the completion of his studies. His views were too original, and his independent character terrified the professors. He also had the misfortune to be born a Jew, and although officially there was no anti-Semitism in Switzerland, racial prejudice, alas, as elsewhere, was not unknown, not to mention a latent chauvinism which his recent naturalization offended.

However, he had to earn his living. He had met a young Hungarian student, Mileva Maritsch, whom he wanted to marry and who would later bear him two sons. After eking out a meager existence in a few temporary posts, he was forced to accept a regular job as an engineer in the Patent Office at Berne.

This work, which was far below his capacity, pleased him. He had to write reports giving the main essentials of the inventions claiming legal protection. This gave him an opportunity of studying fundamentally a number of new ideas in the most varied fields. It also gave him a great deal of freedom, and his leisure could be fruitfully employed on his own work.

It was at Berne that he elaborated his first theories on the Brownian movement, the perfecting of Max Planck's quantum theory, and ultimately the postulates of the special theory of relativity.

2

The First Works of Einstein

AT the beginning of the nineteenth century, the Scottish botanist Robert Brown demonstrated by mixing pollen dust in water that the component particles of that water—until then hypothetical—were subject to incessant movements, moving in irregular zigzags, without the intervention of any external influence such as currents or some other action.

It has been observed elsewhere that the effects of temperature were bound up with these movements: the hotter the water the more the agitation increased in intensity. To maintain, however, that the agitation of molecules increased with hotness was to take the cause for the effect. Today we know that it is the thermal agitation of the molecules which causes the temperature of the water (or any other material), and not the reverse.

In 1902, Einstein reduced to a clear formula this disorderly movement of particles, proving that their mean displacement in a certain direction increased with the square root of the time elapsed. At the same time he showed that the mean kinetic energy of particles in the Brownian movement was the same as for molecules. One could thus, by a simple method, determine the number of molecules per unit volume, i.e. this could be achieved by measuring the distance traveled by the visible particles.

It was an important advance, since it revealed the reality of molecules, which had previously been a matter of controversy.

At the same period Einstein attacked the most controversial

problem of all, that of the nature of light. The surest way of producing light is to heat a solid body. When the thermal content increases above a certain level, varying according to the nature of the material in question—let us say a metal—the object starts to glow dark red and gradually becomes a brilliant white. This signifies that a mixture of the colors of the spectrum occurs in the visible wavelengths emitted. It will be recalled that visible light consists of radiations of different wavelengths or different frequencies ranging from red (for the longest waves, or, if one prefers, the lowest frequencies) to violet (for short waves, or higher frequencies), and always as far as the visible spectrum is concerned, passing systematically through the intermediary colors—orange, yellow, green, blue, and indigo.

In 1900, Max Planck had postulated that the phenomenon of light was accounted for by the oscillation of atoms which took place not in a progressive or continuous manner but, on the contrary, by successive steps—in other words, in a discontinuous manner, once a definite quantity of energy had been acquired. "Radiation," he said, "is apparently emitted or absorbed in lumps of quantity, or *quanta*." This means that below a certain minimum value, as far as each radiation is concerned, there is no emission or absorption of radiation. From this it followed that the energy of the oscillation of an atom could not have an indeterminate value but only values which are multiples of a certain minimum value.*

Today we know that it is the electron, abandoning the "parcel of energy" which allowed it to leave the normal orbit it described around the nucleus of the atom and subsequently rejoining this natural orbit, which is responsible for the emission of radiation.†

Max Planck had only dealt with the mechanism of the emission or absorption of light, showing that these processes could take place only in whole quantities. He had not touched the composition of light rays, and it was still thought that the character of light was undulatory and that a kind of "rigid medium," the ether, in space allowed the propagation of these

---

* h (Planck's constant) $= 6.624 \times 10^{-27}$.

† cf. the author's: *L'Atome* in the *Encyclopédie des Sciences et des Techniques*.

waves by vibration just as any rigid medium (air, water, or metal) allows the propagation of sound waves.

It will be recalled that Huygens' undulatory theory was preferred to Newton's corpuscular theory because it conformed better to experimental observation. Fresnel, Young, and subsequently Maxwell had admirably consolidated this thesis. But at the turn of the century the German physicist Lenard showed that when light strikes the surface of a metal, which as we know today has the effect of freeing the electrons (metallic gleam has no other cause), the energy with which these electrons are expelled does not depend upon the intensity of the rays of light but simply on their color, that is to say, on the frequency of the radiation. To be more precise: whatever the distance at which the source of light is placed, the electrons are expelled at the same speed (although the number of expulsions naturally decreases with the increase of this distance), but on the other hand the speed of the expelled electrons will be greater if the light is violet (short waves, high frequency) than if it were red (long waves, low frequency).

Einstein drew the following conclusion: "Whatever the distance a light of a given color is propagated from the source, it is always formed of the same integral quantities of energy. The sole difference is that the further the light is removed from its source the more scattered the 'shot-gun pellets' that reach the metal: the expulsion of an electron occurs when it has absorbed a whole quantum of radiation."

It was now comprehensible why the distance between the luminous source and the object struck by the ray had no effect on the energy of the electron emitted. It also had to be admitted that the difference in the energy acquired by the electron (greater in the case of violet light and smaller in the case of red light) indicated that the energies of the grains of light of different colors were associated with different quanta.

The "grain of light" was called a photon. An electron which absorbs a violet photon is expelled at a greater speed than one absorbing a red photon (we must not forget that our idea of colors is only an effect of our senses).

With the hypothesis of the discontinuous nature of light, Einstein blazed the trail for a discontinuous conception of fields of force and more particularly of the electromagnetic field. The photon, the grain of light, is the materialization of this field, just as we know that the meson is the materialization of the nuclear field. This inclines us to think that the natural processes are essentially discontinuous. It is possible that we shall eventually establish a unified field theory once we have been able to prove the discontinuity of the gravitational field. It is still probable that biological phenomena revealed in evolution develop by quanta (could not a mutation be a biological quantum?). On the same principle psychism externalizes itself by "successive leaps" in the animal kingdom. In man it attains the "knowledge of existence."

THE SPECIAL THEORY OF RELATIVITY

We shall now deliberately abandon our chronological sequence in order to present as coherently as possible a few aspects of the relativity theories and more particularly those which come within the category of the special theory of relativity. We shall avoid as far as possible mathematical formulae. They will only be used in certain cases when they will easily be understood by the majority of our readers. We could of course dispense with them entirely, because the essentials of what they mean will always be explained by the text.

The first thing we have to realize is that relativity unquestionably tends to translate the realities of the universe. If some of its demonstrations offend "common sense," it is because of the inadequacy of our sensory perceptions on the one hand, and of our scientific education on the other.

I know that it is difficult to convey to young minds that what they see of the world is only an appearance, but we must at least guard against various dogmatic assertions from which evolve all manner of conditionings extremely difficult to eradicate later when, as intelligence develops, the young man or the adult in the light of new experience perceives that one has simply neglected to explain to him the essentials of cosmic phenomena.

Would it be impossible, for example, to indicate that the stars which shine by night are not located "above" the earth (in the sky according to the sacred formula) but that the earth revolves quite simply around a star to which men have arbitrarily given the name of sun? Would it be difficult to explain that the stellar system of which we are part is only a point in space, or rather a point "punctuating space"? The stars do not shine above, *but all around us*. The aspect of the constellations varies according to the longitude of observation at such and such a spot on the globe, whereas the displacement of the heavenly bodies in the course of the year is an appearance due to the movement of the earth (motion of translation) around the particular star, the sun.

But this is not enough. It would be necessary to indicate that the light we receive from the stars *is not transmitted instantaneously* but at a limited velocity (186,000 m/s approx.). We cannot be certain that these stars exist *today* (earth time), when we look at them, but only that they existed there, according to their distance, more than four, eleven, thirty, fifty, or a hundred years ago; and if we use a powerful telescope or a radiotelescope to observe them, we are capturing the invisible wavelengths they emitted thousands, millions, hundreds of millions, or even billions of years ago. . . .

In the realm of the macrocosm, minds would thus be prepared to assimilate the fundamental principles of relativity. We should add that the stars which appear to us immobile, and which all the astronomy books unfortunately continue to call "fixed," are in reality subject to very rapid movements. We cannot observe the latter on account of the distance of these stars, as for example an aircraft flying at an altitude of 30,000 feet (what are 30,000 feet compared with the 6,000 billion miles of a single light year?) at the speed of sound appears to advance very slowly.

From now on the universe already appears to us in a very different light. We feel that it would be impossible to present a static picture of it. At best it would be possible to take a "snapshot" whose representative value would only be in terms of time, that is to say that the photograph would be valid only for the precise moment at which the picture was taken. Not even this is exact, for we have already seen that since the velocity of light is not instantaneous, the stars we see today may quite well have disappeared a long time ago, and others may have been born thousands of years ago without our realizing it.

This is only a summary conception of relativity themes, as we shall see later, but are we not already equipped to understand cosmic reality? This motion of material in the cosmos has its corollary around us, that is to say in the terrestrial domain. It also exists within us since, as we know, life is no more than a form of motion of matter and everything still takes place as though mind was only a new quality. It must be realized that everything is dynamic, even that which we declare to be inert. It is thanks to the incessant motion of the fundamental particles of the atom nucleus that the nuclear power responsible for the cohesion of the nuclei in this same kernel externalizes itself. It is thanks to the motion of the electrons that the electromagnetic force allows molecular configuration on the organic as well as the inorganic plane.

This motion fills the immense void of the microcosm, and because of it matter appears to us to be compact. In actual fact the mass of atoms is almost exclusively represented by the mass of nuclei which compose their kernels (the mass of an electron is only 1,840th part of that of a nucleus, whereas a kernel occupies about a 10,000th part of the space of a whole atom—there are roughly ten million atoms to a length of one millimeter. But what is mass itself? Einstein postulated that it was to some extent concentrated energy, and subsequent experiments have proved this to be true.

Nevertheless, it is not enough to say that mass is energy or vice versa: relativity shows us—and if we reflect on the question of the identity of energy and matter, there is nothing to offend us—that mass increases in terms of its velocity until it becomes "infinite," when the given motion reaches the speed of light.

Now this speed of light, as relativity proves, cannot be reached and certainly cannot be exceeded in the universe. Mass—and this has been established—is augmented with speed, the mass expressing the inertia of energy—another relativity demonstration—so it is obvious that it becomes proportionately difficult to accelerate a mass as its speed augments.

If we accept the following analogy at its face value, we might say that the "heavier" the material ("heavier" is in quotation marks because the weight of a body is only an effect of the earth's attraction, itself a particular aspect of gravitational phenomena), the better it resists any efforts made to displace it. The more massive a body, the more energy will be needed to overcome its inertia, that is to say to "make it move," or to accelerate it. We have known this since Newton, but we did not know that nature imposed the limit which is "c," the universal constant.

Relativity therefore shows what Galileo foresaw, that there is a profound identity between the ponderable mass (weight) and the inert mass. Mass expresses the inertia of matter (we can observe in a tube from which the air has been pumped that a feather and a piece of lead "fall" at the same speed, that is to say with identical acceleration): Relativity proves on the other hand that acceleration (or centrifugal force) can be closely assimilated to gravitational phenomena.

Obviously we cannot expect that all this should be crammed *en bloc* into a young brain, but the child could gradually be prepared—even in the elementary physics classes—for a glimpse of these pregnant truths. He could be told that Euclidian geometry is a splendid monument to human thought but that its postulates are invalidated as soon as theory gives place to practice. For example, with regard to terrestrial measurements on a sphere, the shortest distance between one point and another point cannot be a straight line. To convince ourselves of this let us trace a triangle on a terrestrial globe having as its base two points situated on the equator and as its apex one of the poles, and we shall see that the sum of the inner angles of this triangle does not equal two right angles.

Let us get this into our heads: relativity is not built of mathematical artifices nor is it an abstraction. It *genuinely* translates physical facts.

But the universe being only the combined motion of objects (planets, stars, galaxies, particles, etc.) in space and incidentally the time created by their very presence, it is necessary in order to give a correct representation not only to take into account the three space coordinates (length, breadth, and height) plus a coordinate of time, but also to record the variation of the measurements (or rather the instruments of measurement, which are rays of light) that serve for definition.

These variations are due to the alteration of the standards, that being the function of the various relative speeds (in relation to each other) of objects serving to record such and such a cosmic event, for the proof of the limitation of the speed of light (as opposed to its instantaneous propagation) in the void encourages us to consider the relativity of the idea of simultaneity.

THE INVARIANCE OF THE VELOCITY OF LIGHT

The constancy of the speed of light was proved by numerous experiments, the most famous of which were carried out at the beginning of this century by two Americans, Michelson and Morley. Using special apparatus, the technique of which we shall not bother to describe here, it was their ambition to show on the one hand the existence of the imponderable milieu known as "ether," necessary to explain the transmission of light rays, while on the other hand they hoped to prove that it was possible to calculate the speed of the earth's translation around the sun by addition or subtraction of the said speed to the total of the speed of a ray of light.

Was it not logical to presume that a ray of light traveling at a speed of some 186,000 m/s "launched" in the direction of the earth's translation—18.6 m/s—would reach a total speed of 186,000 + 18.6 m/s whereas, widdershins, the same ray of light would only reach 186,000 − 18.6 m/s?

Now to the general surprise this was not the case. Whichever way the experiment was carried out, nature invalidated this axiom of classical mechanics. In both directions the speed of light remained immutably at 186,000 m/s. By a similar experiment the Dutch astronomer, de Sitter, from his observation of double stars, proved that the speed of light does not depend upon the speed at which the source of the light moves.

Let us be frank: such a statement conflicts with "common sense." It is also contrary to the principles of classical mechanics. We should expect, when we travel at a certain speed toward a source of light, to see our own speed added to that of the light which emanates from it. Now experience shows this is not the case.

When we recede at a certain speed from a source of light— as when the latter recedes from us at a certain speed—we should be able to record a diminution of the intrinsic speed of the light ray, but neither is this the case, as has been proved by experiment.

It is said that the propagation of light is isotropic and that *its speed is constant*. The motions of the source of light have *no influence* on the speed of the radiation emitted.

Einstein showed where classical mechanics erred by the constancy of the velocity of light in space; the spatial measurement (length) and the measurement of time are not the same for observers reputed to be at rest and for the objects observed in motion in relation to these observers (in the same way the measurements change if the observers themselves are in motion in relation to the events observed).

The absolute character of the durations (absolute time) and the absolute character of length (absolute space) should be connected with the existence of infinite speeds, but Einstein postulated that these do not exist in nature. Since it was further proved that light is propagated at a limited speed and that the ray of light (when we speak of light, we must also include invisible as well as the visible wavelengths) is effectively the indispensable intermediary for the realization of all physical measurement, it becomes logical to admit that space "in itself" and time "in itself" according to Newton, Kant, and classical mechanics had no reality.

PREAMBLE TO THE THEORY OF RELATIVITY

Space is not a mathematical absolute; it is only the measure of distance from material points to other material points. Nor is time a mathematical absolute; it is the measure of the motion of objects in space.

Space therefore only exists by reason of the presence of objects such as galaxies, stars, planets, nebulae, meteors, or any particle however infinitesimal it may be. In the terrestrial domain space is actually no more than a measure between certain arbitrarily chosen points, and the whole of geometry is based on such concepts. When we come to the extremely reduced framework of molecules, atoms, or even the nuclei of these atoms, space is still the measure of the distances between certain of their constituent particles in constant vibration.

If we wish to measure the length of a road, nothing is easier than to provide ourselves with a surveyor's chain (it can also be done by optical method, but let us deliberately choose the simpler method). If we wish to measure a field, the same chain will suffice, and taking into account the length and breadth of the field, it will be easy to calculate its area. If we wish to arrive at the cubic content of a room, we must interpose a third spatial coordinate, the height of the room.

These three spatial coordinates, defined in the main by Descartes, are known as the Cartesian orthogonal coordinates. They suffice for any measurements of space within the framework of Euclidian geometry (that is to say, supposing the existence of "straight" lines). Spatial measures being static, it is understood that the chosen frames of reference are rigid.

But suppose we wish to determine the position of an aircraft flying "somewhere in the Pacific," by the aid of radio messages. We shall ask the pilot "to give us his bearing," that is to say, to tell us on what degrees of latitude and longitude he happens to be. In order that his position may be plotted accurately with reference to the earth we must obviously ask him to tell us his altitude. We shall thus have our three spatial coordinates: length, breadth, and height.

But is this enough? Obviously not. None of these indications will have any meaning unless we can determine the date and the hour at which the measurements were taken, since the aircraft is not a static but a dynamic object. And this is how at a first approximation time intervenes as a fourth coordinate: it is not integrated with the spatial measurements but is added, and the same applies to relativity, at least, schematically.

As Paul Langevin expressed it: "We do not maintain that time is a fourth dimension of space; we say that kinematics take care of events, and that in order to fix an event we have to recognize four qualities—three spatial and one time coordinate."

But what is time? As we saw at the beginning of this chapter it is the measurement of the motion of objects in space. All man's machines for measuring time (the calendar and clocks for daily use) are based on the movements of the solar system, that is to say on the earth's translation around the sun or on the rotation of the globe itself. What we call a year is a measure of the motion of the earth in its orbit; what we call a day is the measure of the rotating motion of our planet; what we call an hour is an arbitrary division of this same day into twenty-four parts, while a minute is a division of the hour into sixty parts, etc.

But an hour is also an arc of 15° in the apparent daily rotation of the celestial sphere, and we can already see how space and time can closely interlock without being identified with each other. A light-year, a spatial measurement, is merely the measure of the distance traveled by a ray of light in one of our terrestrial years.

In kinematics (and kinematics rule both the macrocosm and the microcosm) there is no absolute spatial and absolute temporal relation, but events represented by a space-time relation.

"What we call an event," according to Eddington, "is a point in space-time, that is to say a determined spot taken at a determined instant." Einstein, however, insists that by this we must understand that "the world being the theater of isolated events, each event can be determined by four numbers, which are respectively the positional coordinates, x, y, and z and the coordinate of time, t."

The world represented thus is a continuum, "for each event we can consider another as close as we wish and whose coordinates x', y', z', t', differ from the preceding coordinates as little as we like."

Let us say, before we leave the subject of terrestrial time, that our natural "clock," the earth in its orbital movement, is subject to other rather mysterious variations and that these variations can be verified thanks to the vibrations of atoms (notably the atom of cesium), but the existence of atomic clocks does not alter the fact that terrestrial time is a *local* and not a *universal* time.

The wavelengths of the atoms used by our physicists and astronomers would be seen to vary if they were accelerated to a great speed. They would also be seen to vary (the slowing down of the clocks) if these atoms were placed as we shall see later in a gravitational field more intense than the terrestrial field of gravitation.

But what is the significance of space if one does not indicate in relation to what this speed is measured? Or again, what do movement and in consequence the measures of space and time signify if one does not indicate the criteria from which they are obtained, or better still, if one cannot define their "standards" beforehand?

The principle of relativity was not Einstein's brainchild. Galileo had stated it explicitly in the following terms: *"The laws of mechanics are the same for all systems moving uniformly"; "uniformly"* signifying at a constant velocity.

Einstein completed this in the following way: *"All the phenomena of nature, all the laws of nature, are identical for all systems moving uniformly, relative to each other."*

The fundamental role of the velocity of light in space by reason of its invariance was clearly defined. The latter (the velocity of light in space) became the sole absolute from which space-time could be gauged. It alone allowed an accurate account to be given of cosmic events. As Einstein demonstrated, its limitation implied the relativity of time, the relativity of space, and the relativity of the mass. But first and foremost we must understand that what we call velocity or movement has no significance except in relation to something. Both Galileo and Newton were well aware of this before Einstein, and let us say at the risk of being repetitive: the movements of the earth, for example, would be absolutely indecipherable for its inhabitants if our globe were entirely isolated, we do not say in space, since space is not a thing in itself, but in an inconceivable void. Therefore, there is no such thing as absolute movement, but only *relative* movements.

If our reasoning were not *a priori* based on an absurdity (since we have just seen that a movement can only be relative), we should say that the isolated earth could travel through the imaginary void at a vertiginous speed (in a *nonaccelerated* uniform movement—we shall see in the chapter on the general theory of relativity the value of the italics) and that it would appear, to those living on its surface, completely immobile. Moreover, did not the scientists of antiquity believe it to be immobile, despite its velocity of translation of some 18.6 m/s and its rotation speed of some 1,525 ft. per sec.?

For them it was the sun (likewise the pseudo-heavenly vault studded with stars) which revolved around it, and from the relativistic point of view there is nothing to stop us believing this today *if we did not know that this contradicts cosmic reality.* (Certain people, incidentally, tried to impose this belief, forgetting the essential—that relativity allows us to translate real facts and that it is not metaphysical.) From this postulate a traveler propelled from the earth in a space rocket could, at the end of the acceleration phase and as it advanced ballistically in the interplanetary pseudo-void, i.e. in conformity with the Galilean principles of inertia, say that he and

ermann Einstein, the physicist's father   Maja Einstein, his sister

A portrait on a cup of
Albert Einstein as a child

Albert Einstein and Mileva, his first wife

The "Berne Academy". Einstein is at extreme right

he alone was the "center" of the universe: that he was "immobile" in space, while the earth sped away from him at a given velocity. . . .

To sum up, let us say that the movement of heavenly bodies, including that of our earth, can be described only in relation to each other. In space there is no privileged direction, and the incessant movements of bodies in space-time render a static representation of the cosmic universe entirely illusory. The latter, as Einstein has shown, can only be a space-time continuum. We shall revert to this subject later.

It remains that for the convenience of calculations and representations the observer (or the laboratory in which the observer operates; the earth or any other system may be considered as such) can be "considered fixed," just as in astronomy we speak of fixed stars without taking the terms to the letter; the stellar "background" being comparable with an astronomical table to which the astronomer refers to locate an event. Without discarding the framework of relativity—quite to the contrary—the scientist can and should arbitrarily choose his "frame of reference," or system of axes of coordinates, allowing the plotting of the position of a point in space.

According to Einstein, every description of events in space *demands the use of a rigid body to which these events can be referred.* It must also be understood that events are capable of being interpreted differently, whence their relativity. For as Einstein explains: "Suppose I were standing at the window in the compartment of a train traveling at uniform speed and I dropped a stone without propulsion on to the permanent way. I shall see, ignoring the influence exercised by the resistance of air, the stone fall in a straight line. But a passerby who observes the fact from the road will see that the falling stone describes a parabola. I now ask: are the 'loci' traversed by the stone really situated on a straight line or on a parabola? Furthermore, what in this instance signifies movement in 'space'?"

Let us, for the moment, says Einstein, dismiss the obscure term "space" which, if we are honest, we cannot really envisage. In its place let us put "movement" in relation to a "frame of reference" for practical purposes rigid. By substituting for this "frame of reference" the idea of a "system of coordinates," which is useful for mathematical description, we can say: "The stone in relation to a system of coordinates rigidly bound to the compartment describes a straight line, but in relation to a system of coordinates rigidly bound to the ground, a parabola."

This example shows quite clearly, concludes Einstein, that there is no such thing as a trajectory in itself (i.e. a trajectory describing the body), but only a trajectory in relation to a determined frame of reference.

Nevertheless, a *complete* description of the movement will only be realized when we have indicated how the body changes place *with time,* i.e. it is absolutely necessary to specify for each point of the trajectory at what particular moment the body was actually there.

But is this all? No, these indications must be complemented by a definition of time so that these temporal values by virtue of this definition—and in principle—may be considered as observable dimensions, in other words, as the results of measurements.

Given that the only way of interpreting an event is to "see" it (or to record it on a receiver of electromagnetic waves, whether the latter be a camera, supplementing our vision, or a radiotelescope, etc.), and that the light, or the electromagnetic waves which are comparable, does not propagate instantaneously, but at a limited velocity (186,000 m/s), would different observers obtain identical spatial and temporal representations?

Certainly not. Experiments compel us to admit that it is necessary to take into account what has been called *"a contraction of the rods"* and a *"slowing down of the clocks,"* in terms of the velocities (in relation to observers considered fixed) of the movements under consideration, the result being analogous if the observers are in movement relative to the events observed.

The invariance of the velocity of light in space, the verification that this velocity cannot be reached or surpassed, as we shall see later, implies the abandonment of an unlimited possibility of the addition of velocities according to the laws of classical mechanics. The Michelson-Morley experiment, repeated and checked, shows indisputably that the speed of the source of light has no influence whatsoever on the speed of the propagation of the ray of light.

Einstein realized that a new transformation had to be found. This rule would allow a scientist to describe the relations between systems in movement, so that the results of the observation would correspond to the facts observed.

He found this new rule in a series of equations worked out by the Dutch physicist Lorentz in which, starting from the premise that since the velocity of light can in no circumstances be exceeded in nature, a clock attached to a system in movement runs at a different rate from that of a clock considered to be immobile, and that a standard measuring rod applied to a system in movement modifies its length in relation to the velocity of the system: the clock shows that the speed increases and the measuring rod shrinks in the direction of its own movement.

All this, of course, agrees with regard to the fixed observer, and the phenomena would appear to him identical if the events were considered fixed relative to himself, who would then also be in movement relatively. But as Louis de Broglie points out: Einstein saw in the Lorentz transformation: "Not a simple mathematical device such as had been made before him, but the very expression of the liaison which exists physically between space and time."

The brilliant creator of wave-mechanics comments: "According to the ideas still ruling on the absolute character of space-time, the variables x', y', z', t' of the Lorentz transformation cannot coincide with the true space-time coordinates in the new system of reference. Lorentz only considered them as a type of fictitious variable facilitating certain calculations. Nevertheless, getting very close to the true solution of the problem with the aid of the variable t', he defined a certain local time. . . . For Einstein, the formulae of the Lorentz transformation were not simple mathematical relations defining a change of variables, convenient for studying the equations of electromagnetism; they were the expression of the relation which exists *physically* between the coordinates of space and time of two Galilean observers (i.e. in uniform movement of translation).

Showing that the nonexistence of signals propagated with an infinite velocity entails the impossibility of verifying the simultaneity of two events occurring at distant points, Einstein analyzed the way in which observers bound to the same system in movement of uniform translation would, by synchronizing their clocks, be able by exchanges of signals to define a simultaneity in their frame of reference, but that this simultaneity would be valid for them alone, and the events which would appear to them to be simultaneous would not be so identified by observers in movement in relation to them.

"Into this reasoning," explains Louis de Broglie, "came the fact that no signal can be propagated with a velocity greater than that of light in space. Space and time cease to have an absolute character, but space-time which reunites them preserves this character. In space-time each observer divides his space and time in his own way and the Lorentz transformation shows how these different divisions are related to each other."

THE SYSTEM OF COORDINATES AND THE LORENTZ TRANSFORMATION

Since the days of ancient Greece it has been known that in order to describe the movement of a body it must be related to another body.*

The movement of a train is described in relation to the ground, as is that of a car, and as we have seen, the same applies to an aircraft whose position has to be determined in relation to latitude, longitude, and altitude (plus a coordinate of terrestrial time). With regard to the position of a planet, a meteorite, a comet, a star, a nebula, or a galaxy, it is necessary to refer to what is still wrongly called "the sphere of the fixed stars," i.e. the visible stellar constellations as a whole, seen with the naked eye or through a telescope. Nevertheless, in physics the bodies to which the movements of the bodies are related in space are called *"systems of coordinates."*

The laws of Galilean and Newtonian mechanics can only be formulated by using a system of coordinates.

The state of movement of a system of coordinates cannot be chosen arbitrarily; if the laws of mechanics are to prove exact, the system must not be subject either to rotation or acceleration. The system of coordinates used in classical mechanics is known as the "inertial system." As long as it is

* In the following pages certain repetitions will be found. The author considered this more practical than using back references, taking into account the effort of abstraction already demanded of the reader.

simply a question of these laws of classical mechanics (non-relativistic), the system of coordinates used is not limited by nature, but to one condition complying with the following proposition: "A system of coordinates moving in the same direction and with the same velocity as a system of inertia is itself an inertial system."

The first principle of the special theory of relativity states: *"Every law of nature which is true in relation to a system of coordinates K must also hold true for any system K', provided that K and K' are uniformly translated with respect to each other."*

The second principle upon which the special theory of relativity rests is that of the invariance of the velocity of light in space, as propounded in the previous chapter. But as we have seen, these two principles do not appear compatible. Einstein succeeded in establishing a logical agreement between them by introducing "a change in kinematics, in other words a change in the doctrine of the physical laws of space-time (Lorentz transformation)."

The Lorentz transformation* expressed the relationship between distances and times observed in systems in movement in relation to those observed with systems approximately static.

"Let us suppose," writes Lincoln Barnett, from whom we have borrowed the substance of this paragraph, "that a system or a given body is moving in a certain direction: according to the old principle of the addition of velocities, a distance x' calculated in relation to the system in motion in the direction of this movement, is defined by its relation to the length x, calculated in relation to an approximately motionless system by the equation: $x' = x +$ (or $-$) vt (v representing the speed of the system in movement and t representing time)."

The dimensions y' and z', measured in relation to the system in movement to the right angle of x', and to the right angle of the one in relation to the other (i.e. in height and breadth), are relative to the dimensions y and z on the approximately stationary system according to the formula $y' = y$ and $z' = z$.

Finally, an interval of time t' measured in relation to the

* We must apologize for the introduction of a few mathematical formulae for the purpose of explaining the Lorentz transformation, but the nonmathematical reader can skip this section.

system in movement is, in relation to the interval of time *t*, measured in relation to the approximately immobile system according to the formula $t' = t$.

In other terms, the distances and the times are not modified in classical physics by the speed of the system envisaged, *but then the phenomena are no longer correctly interpreted, and the two first principles of the special theory of relativity are contravened.*

The equations which take into account the Lorentz transformation preserve the velocity of light as a universal constant, but they modify all the consequences by giving them to the speed of each frame of reference.

In other words the Lorentz transformation reduces the distances and times observed in systems in movement to the conditions of the observer at rest (in relation to these systems), by taking *c* the velocity of light as a constant for every observer.

The following are the relevant mathematical equations of the Lorentz transformations:

$$(1) \quad x' = \frac{x - vt}{\sqrt{1 - (v^2/c^2)}}$$

$$(2) \quad y' = y \qquad . \qquad (3) \quad z' = z$$

$$(4) \quad t' = \frac{t - (v^2/c^2)x}{\sqrt{1 - (v^2/c^2)}}$$

"It should be noted," says Barnett, "that in the old law of transformation, the dimensions y' and z' were not modified by the movement. It will be seen therefore that, if the velocity of the system in movement *v* is small relative to the velocity of light *c*, then the Lorentz equations are reduced and we return to the old principle of adding the velocities. But when the magnitude of *v* approaches that of *c*, the value x' and the value t' are radically modified."

THE RELATIVITY OF SIMULTANEITY AND ITS CONSEQUENCES

Simultaneously means "at the same time." Simultaneity is the existence of several actions, of several events at the same moment. But can we speak of simultaneity with regard to the observation of some particular cosmic event? Relativity replies with a categorical "No," taking into account the noninstantaneous propagation of a ray of light, the only valid criterion for recording these events.

If I maintain that tonight at midnight I saw Sirius and the moon appear simultaneously from behind a cloud, my assertion would have no significance. Already as regards the moon, situated about 225,000 miles from the earth, I should have a lag of rather more than 1 second as far as the simultaneity of the event measured by my own watch is concerned. (The moon would have emerged from behind the cloud at a little more than one second before midnight, but this lag is of course too insignificant to be noticed.) It is quite a different matter in the case of Sirius, whose rays I recorded would have been emitted nearly nine years ago. (Sirius is situated at 2.7 parsecs of the solar system; a parsec represents 3.66 light years; a light year, the distance traveled by light in one year, is equivalent to approximately 6,200 billion miles).

If Proxima Centauri, the nearest star to the earth, disappeared from our sky *today* (by our earth time), it would mean that it had disintegrated more than four years ago (this multiple system is 4.3 light years from the solar system). On the contrary, if the explosion occurred *today* (earth time), we should know nothing about it for another 4.3 years. We should still see Proxima Centauri shining for another 4.3 years. . . .

When we see the birth of a nova lighting up a whole galaxy some three billion light years away, we should remember that the phenomenon took place when life on this earth was only just beginning.

But this grandiose and terrifying treatise should not make us lose sight of the fact that the relativity of simultaneity holds a very precise place in the Einsteinian theories, and in particular it explains what is known as "the contraction of the rods."

THE CONTRACTION OF MEASURING RODS

What defines for us the apparent length of a measuring rod is the demarcated image on our retina of the two rays coming from the two ends of the rod. These rays arrive simultaneously on our retina.

There is no doubt as to this simultaneity while the rod is at rest in front of us or if we stand motionless in front of it. But this simultaneity becomes much less certain if the rod flashes past us at full speed.

Suppose we wish to know the length of our rod: we take for example a unit of 6 inches and mark it on the rod as many times as is necessary to "measure" it, that is to say we begin by making the end of our unit coincide very precisely with one end of the rod, and then having carefully marked with a pencil the first 6 inches measured, we place the end of the unit on this mark and repeat the performance. Let us say, for our convenience, that the rod is exactly six units in length, in other words, three feet.

This operation is obviously only possible when the measuring rod is at rest. Let us replace this rod, a measure become an object of measurement, by a train standing in a station, whose length we want to know. We shall meet with no difficulty since we only have to run our rod the necessary number of times along the train from the front of the engine to the end of the rear coach in order to find the total length. Once more for the sake of convenience, let us say that we have used our rod a hundred times, end to end, which gives us the total length of the train as 300 feet.

But now we are asked to verify whether the length of the train is the same when in motion as when it was stationary. How do we do this? Naturally we cannot place the rod in all haste on the sides of the cars as they flash past. There is only one possible solution—the optical method of measuring. We choose a straight part of the track, then having planted a stake at a certain selected spot (let us say a red stake), we measure 300 feet of rail and at the precise spot where these 300 feet end, we plant a second stake, this time a blue one. The direction of the train's displacement will be from the red to the blue stake.

We must now move far enough away to be able to take in *simultaneously* the coincidence between the passage of the front of the engine and the blue stake and the passage of the end of the rear coach and the red stake; in other words, we must place ourselves at a sufficient distance at the center of the total distance to be measured, let us say 250 feet from both stakes.

The train now passes us at full speed, say about 80 m.p.h. When the front of the engine coincides with the blue stake, it sends a ray of light (leading ray) which coincides with the ray coming from the blue stake. *At the same time* the ray from the end of the rear coach reaches our eye, but will this ray coincide in time with the ray from the red stake?

Certainly not. In fact the leading ray recedes from the front of the engine at the same speed as the rear ray from the end of the rear coach. Let us recall, as the Michelson-Morley experiment showed, that the velocity of light is not affected by the velocity of the source of light, i.e. for our fixed observers on the railway embankment the propagation of the ray of light is accomplished in both instances at a constant velocity of 186,000 m/s; the leading ray does not reach us at 186,000 m/s minus 80 m/h, the speed at which the train is receding from us, any more than the rear ray reaches us at 186,000 m/s, plus 80 m/h, the speed at which the same train approaches us, but both rays reach us at the immutable speed c (universal constant), i.e. 186,000 m/s approx.

However, the front extremity of the engine recedes from view while the rear extremity approaches. In consequence (without its intrinsic value varying), the leading ray propagates toward our eye more slowly than the rear ray *without our being able to perceive it, since on their arrival we find the same speed in both rays* (the result, we must repeat, of the propagation of light at a constant velocity).

There is no question of doubt: the rear ray which reaches our eye at the same time as the leading ray must have left the end of the rear coach later than the leading ray left the front of the engine, so, when we see the front of the engine coinciding with the blue stake we shall simultaneously see the rear of the last coach having slightly passed the red stake: the length of the train traveling at full speed will undoubtedly appear less than the distance between the two stakes—in other words, the train will not seem as long when it is in motion as when it was stationary.

Such an example, of course, is purely theoretical. The difference in length of a mobile object will be imperceptible at such a low speed as 80 m/h, but if we set the experiment in the context for which it is valid, i.e. on the level of the macrocosm or even of the microcosm (where particles reach speeds approaching that of light), it accounts for the reality of the *contraction of the measuring rods* revealed by the laws of relativity. The contraction will be proportionately more apparent as the speed of the mobile object concerned increases. In other words, the object observed and measured will seem even more shortened by its speed and in the direction of the latter, in relation to the observer, as this speed approaches that of light. The phenomenon will be recorded identically if it is the observer who is in movement before the object.

It should be noticed that if the object (or observer) could attain the speed of light (which invalidates relativity) this object for the observer considered at rest (or the immobile object for the observer in movement) would measure exactly zero.

Let us say at once that the shortcomings of our optical sensory perception have nothing to do with it, as when a distortion of the image of a racing motor car passing us at full speed is produced (on the contrary, the image appears to us distended). It is a true contraction of length (in relation to the observer) established by the Lorentz transformation.

The contraction of the measuring rods is true to the extent that it translates a metric property of space-time. (We have already seen that neither time nor space is a mathematical absolute as was formerly believed.) But this contraction has no absolute value in itself (an astronaut approaching the speed of light in a rocket of the future propelled with matter-antimatter reactions will not see his rocket diminish in length). The contraction only represents the different manner in which the observers place the ends of their rods: two observers in relative movement with a different idea of simultaneity (for example, because of different distances from the object observed) would be in disagreement as to the length of the objects.

What then is "true measurement"? We shall see later that this question is of no importance, for it implies that cosmic measures should conform to terrestrial measures. But relativity professes to give us an objective representation of natural phenomena; this was previously unattainable because of an erroneous *interpretation* of our sensory impressions.*

There is no doubt that a true measure is one that can be made with measuring apparatus, which corresponds to norms of standardization previously established (comparisons): thus one meter is a ten-millionth part of a quarter of the earth's meridian, and there is no doubt that this standard of measure is valid (approximatively and under normal conditions of temperature as far as the said instruments and the objects are concerned) for carrying out any static measurement (experimenter and object to be measured) at a global level.

But if we wish to measure cosmic events *our meter, or rather our measuring rod, will be the ray of light,* and it is to this that we should undoubtedly refer. It is the ray of light alone which translates for us the reality of observed facts; logically, then, we should accept its norms and respect the results obtained.

We must realize above all that cosmic events are not static but essentially dynamic, and just as in our example of the determination of the position of an aircraft (there is nothing relativist in this example) we had to introduce a coordinate of time, this temporal coordinate becomes absolutely indispensable for a correct interpretation of any cosmic event whatsoever (from the macrocosm to the microcosm).

But relativity shows that although the three spatial coordinates and the fourth coordinate of time are used separately in the equations, time and space are not independent: time is not a mathematical absolute; its measurement depends on relative movements in space just as measurements of distance depend on times proper to each observer.

Paul Couderc writes: "Relativity leads to a close fusion of space and time known as space-time, whose components are relative space and relative time. From all this relativity we shall see emerge a new absolute, *the interval* between two events which represents a more profound reality."

This interval of things in four-dimensional space-time is a

*And not because of a momentary deficiency of our senses.

sort of conglomerate, an amalgam of space and time: its components may vary, but it itself remains invariable. What has to be admitted—for it has been proved by experiment—is that the distance in time and the distance in space of two closely allied events both increase or diminish as the speed of the observer diminishes or increases.

THE SLOWING DOWN OF THE CLOCKS

For a long time various philosophies, too often based on metaphysics or solely on intuitions or sensations that no experiment has proved, have tried to define time (for us the only valid philosophy is one which does not systematically eliminate science but on the contrary extends it). Now time outside metaphysics is strictly nothing in itself. It is nothing apart from the movement it serves to measure. No other definition confusing time with the duration of beings (Bergson in particular realized this) can be acceptable in the sense in which both Newton and Kant understood it. Everything happens as though an absolute entity free of temporal criteria existed, energy (or movement) capable of giving birth to mass (or matter) from which our ideas of space and time are born. Thus the stars are born, develop, and die after being accompanied or not by planetary retinues. On the planets of the stellar systems, under certain conditions, matter termed inert can organize itself into biological complexes, which themselves are born, evolve, reproduce, and die. From complication to complication a new quality of movement of matter externalizes to the point of giving the matter (or rather to life, a form of the movement of matter) consciousness of existing. Whence, perhaps, in the most evolved creature we know, in other words, man, the firmly anchored belief of existence not only in the present but even *for all eternity* and sometimes *since eternity*.

But alas, this eminently transient, profoundly esoteric, and religious idea is not based on the slenderest of presumptions *when it is a case of the survival of the individual*. It is quite a different matter with the law of the conservation of energy mass, and the latter could not even be invalidated by the idea of a world evolving toward greater entropy (for our part we find this difficult to accept, believing rather in a possibility of regeneration of the mass-energy from physical processes as yet unknown).

In any case, time is considered as having its own objective existence, independent of bodies and phenomena; this Newtonian time which, like space, should exist "even if the bodies and the phenomena disappeared"; this Kantian time "a form of our sensitivity" has been dispossessed of its absolute (like space in the identical sense) since the fertile application of relativity theories.

We have already referred to the time of our clocks—a terrestrial measure whose standard is the movement of the globe around its central axis. Even more than for space, the relativity of simultaneity is apparent here. With it our "now" has no value with regard to cosmic phenomena: what we capture "at the moment" of stellar images are rays of light from stars which may have disappeared tens, hundreds, thousands, hundreds of thousands, millions, or billions of years ago.

The place these heavenly bodies seem to occupy in space (which they punctuate) would lead us to a false interpretation of the space-time universe if we did not take into account their *respective* distances and their *respective* movements in time and space not only from our point of view—terrestrial observers considered at rest—but from the point of view of *reciprocal* positions and *reciprocal* movements of these cosmic "objects" in the space-time continuum.

Our famous "constellations" are only an "effect of perspective." They have often changed aspect since man has been able to observe them, and they will continue to do so. We must not forget that they are formed of stars located at an immense distance from each other and that only the effect of perspective makes them appear to us as groups.

What significance now could we give to the measurements taken of a comet with its tail unfurled if we locate it in the sky, its head and tail *simultaneously* brushing such and such a star, one of which is ten and the other a hundred light years away; both stars, because of their apparently identical magnitudes, would appear to us to be situated at the same distance from our solar system.

The relativity of simultaneity, itself determined by the limitation of the velocity of light, intervenes therefore in the measurement of time as it intervened in the measurement of space. The existence of an absolute time would in fact impose the possibility of instantaneous propagation of a ray of light (the sole instrument of measurement) and further of the existence of infinite velocities which is in flagrant contradiction to the facts observed.

Let us try to solve the problem with the aid of the example of our train which we used to explain the contraction of the rods. We still have before our eyes our observers placed beside the track at equal distance from the red and blue stakes, and the rectilinear strip of railway track on which our train will pass at full speed in the direction red stake———→blue stake. We will equip each of these stakes with an electric bulb, both of them lighting up at the same time with the aid of a common switch. It is clear when this switch is pulled that the two flashes will appear simultaneously for us, the observer considered at rest sitting on the ballast along the railway line.

But would it be the same for an observer whom we install very uncomfortably in the middle of the center car of the moving train with a mirror in front of him, oriented so that he can see at the same time the light from the red and the light from the blue stakes? Certainly not. For when the train moves away from the red stake in the direction of the blue it is obvious that the red light will be reflected in his mirror a fraction of time later than the blue light. The proof lies in the fact that could we conceive a train reaching the speed of light (i.e. a speed equal to the speed of the propagation of an electromagnetic wave, or, if you prefer, of a photon), the red light could never be reflected in the mirror of the observer in movement of translation relative to the observer (ourselves on the ballast considered at rest). If there is a simultaneity of events for the latter, it does not exist for the observer in movement. For him the switching on of the blue light would have preceded that of the red. Let us stress that if the propagation of light were instantaneous and not "at a constant velocity," there would be simultaneity in every case.

This experiment shows *de rigueur* that we cannot possibly entertain an identical notion of time according to whether we are at rest relative to the event observed or in motion relative to the same event, which Einstein expresses as follows: *"Each frame of reference or system of coordinates has its own time."* And he adds: *"Unless the body to which a statement of time*

*refers is specified there is no significance in the statement of
the time of an event."*

To return to our example, we can say that everything happens as though the time which elapsed during the passage of
the train between the two stakes had been less for the observer-traveler than for the observer at rest alongside the
track. Now can this "shorter time" to accomplish an identical
journey mean anything else than the slowing down of its
clock? It is obvious that if in a car, regulated to travel at a
constant speed of 60 m/h, and equipped with a perfectly
synchronized chronometer (with the quartz clock of the Paris
Observatory), I travel at exactly 1 mile in 1 minute, with a
clock which loses time on the other hand, what I believed to
have been a mile, if I rely solely on my measurement of time,
will be a slightly longer distance. Conversely, with a chronometer that gains time I should not have quite covered a
mile. . . .

It is clear that a clock on which the hand records a smaller
number of seconds to measure an event identical to that
measured by a clock indicating a larger number of seconds, is
indisputably a clock which loses time.

K being the observer on the track and K' being the observer-traveler, Einstein wrote: "Let us imagine a clock showing seconds permanently at rest at the place of K'. Let two
successive ticks of this clock be ($t = 0$ and $t' = 1$). The former is the fourth equation of the Lorentz transformation
giving for its ticks:

$$(1)\ t = 0$$

$$(2)\ t' = \frac{1}{\sqrt{1 - \dfrac{v^2}{c^2}}}$$

In relation to K the clock is moving with velocity v. In relation to this frame of reference the interval of time which

separates two successive ticks is not one second but $\dfrac{1}{\sqrt{1 - \dfrac{v^2}{c^2}}}$

of a second—in other words a slightly shorter time. As a result

of its movement the clock goes a little more slowly than when
it is at rest."

THE CONSTANCY OF LIGHT "C" AND THE
CONTRACTION OF SPACE-TIME

Speed is space covered during a period of time. Space and
time are both relative but speed is strictly limited in the
universe to the speed of light in space, 186,000 m/s. How can
this be conceived? Suppose from the earth which we will
arbitrarily declare as immobile (this is our perfect right in
relativity), we launch a photon space rocket capable of achiev-
ing the speed of 124,000 m/s. After the accelerating phase
and when traveling through space in uniform motion at this
speed of 124,000 m/s measured from the earth, the astronaut
from the relativist point of view has the same right as ourselves to consider that he is immobile.

Now aboard his spaceship he has a second photon rocket
also capable of reaching a speed of 124,000 m/s, and he fires
it. Now here is a second rocket after its own phase of
acceleration eating up space in turn at a speed of 124,000
m/s *in relation to the astronaut.*

But for the terrestrial observer, that is to say, in relation to
the earth which we have considered as at rest, what according to his instruments utilizing the Doppler effect will be the
actual speed of this second rocket? One would be tempted
to reply 248,000 m/s, according to the norms of classical
mechanics. But not at all. According to the *physical* observations recorded by the earth instruments, the speed of the
second rocket will be under 124,000 m/s, which incidentally
is strictly corroborated by the Lorentz transformation quoted
above.

The reason that the astronaut thinks (and he is entitled to
think this) the rocket he has launched has reached 124,000
m/s relative to himself is because his time is quite different
from time on earth.

After the physiological perturbations caused by the launching of the rocket, he rediscovered a rhythm of life absolutely
identical to the one he knew on earth. His heart beats continue at an identical rate, as he can verify by comparing them

with the movement of the second hand on his instrument panel chronometer. For him this "different" time is therefore absolutely normal.

But if the earth dwellers could record the beating of the astronaut's heart, they would find that it had slowed down compared with the time he was living among them down below. *In relation to their own clocks, atomic or otherwise,* the astronaut's time has slowed down (and the time of the second rocket has slowed down even more). *In relation to them* the component atoms of the astronaut's body and those of the rocket matter—the typical clocks of the relativist—indisputably reveal a contraction of time (the waves they emit tend toward red). Both the heart and the pulse of the spaceman compared with the heart of the observer below beat slower, and his metabolism has been slowed down.

Paul Langevin, in his famous demonstration (Langevin's traveler), has shown that a man leaving the earth at a speed inferior by one twenty-thousandth to that of light in space, traveling for a year of his own time and returning at the same speed to land on the globe (i.e. two years after his departure measured by his own clock), would find that the earth had aged by two centuries (e.g. at three generations to a century); the great-grandson of his daughter born on the day of his departure when he was thirty years old would be one hundred, whereas he himself would only be thirty-two. . . .

If we exclude the technical difficulties of the building of the spaceship and its launching, and the time needed in acceleration to achieve its ultimate speed, the theory is irrefutable. It can be verified in nuclear physics; the mesons (μ), unstable particles originating from the disintegration of the mesons (π), have an average life of 2.2 millionths of a second (they then disintegrate spontaneously into an electron and a neutrino). Now in the secondary cosmic radiation where they are found, as a result of processes of transmutation caused by the impact of the primary radiation on the particles of the upper atmosphere, these mesons (μ), before disintegrating, travel distances far superior (several miles, up to 6) to those they should achieve, taking into account their span of life at rest and their speed, which approaches that of light. It is this speed, relative to the observer, which is responsible for the slowing down of the clock (we must not forget that every particle in vibration is a clock) of the meson and therefore for the prolongation of its span of life relative to the same particle at rest.

THE VELOCITY OF LIGHT AND THE INCREASE OF ENERGY MASS

The theory of relativity shows that at the speed of light all length should reduce itself to zero and every clock stop, but this is not all. Every mass ought to grow indefinitely, or, if you prefer, to present an infinite inertia to every effort to accelerate it.

Mass is only concentrated energy and all energy possesses a mass. Thanks to energy one can increase the speed of a mobile object, of a particle or displace a mass at rest.

This "contributive" energy is necessary by reason of the inertia of matter. Newton's law of inertia reads as follows: *"A body sufficiently distant from other bodies remains in its state of repose or of rectilinear and uniform movement."* Galileo had already shown by his experiments with falling bodies that all types of matter whatever the composition, are attracted towards the ground to the same extent of time (in a laboratory tube in which a vacuum has been obtained it will be found that a feather and a piece of lead will "fall" at the same speed).

Anticipating a little the general relativity theory let us say that *"mass appears to us today as the inertia of a certain quantity of energy."*

In his law of the conservation of mass Lavoisier argued that *"the mass of a body conserves itself integrally whatsoever the changes to which the body is subjected."*

This is "almost" true when it is a question of experiments carried out within the framework of speeds possible to realize with our human techniques, which are very small compared with the speed of light. An intercontinental rocket does not at the moment exceed 5,000 m/h. Space rockets in orbit after being accelerated by a succession of boosters reach a speed of a little under 7 m/s relative to the earth considered at rest (as opposed to 186,000 m/s, the velocity of light in space).

In calculations of these speeds the variation of the mass hardly enters, and the equation of classical mechanics

$v + v' = v''$ remains approximately valid. We can say that taking into account the speed necessary to overcome atmospheric resistance a five-stage rocket takes off at the speed of 1 m/s; once the base of the rocket becomes detached, the four remaining rockets, profiting by this initial speed, now achieve (by the firing of rocket No. 2) a speed of 1.5 m/s, or 2.5 m/s in all. When the second rocket is jettisoned in turn, thanks to the firing of the rocket No. 3 capable of realizing 2 m/s, we get 4.5 m/s for the two remaining rockets, and eventually $4.5 + 2.5 = 7$ m/s; $7 + 4 = 11$ m/s.

Admittedly these figures are very theoretical, but they are valid by and large to quote as an example of the addition of speeds according to classic mechanics; although it exists, the change of mass is so small that it does not affect the working out of the basic calculations.

It is quite another matter when we come to cosmic speeds, for example, in subnuclear particles.

We have seen that the contraction of space-time became apparent in the case of mesons which were very closely studied by Ives and Stilwell between 1938 and 1941. But as early as 1831 Fizeau stated after studying the propagation of light in flowing water, itself moving with a certain speed, that the speed of light (which is only 137,020 m/s in water) was not increased by the total speed of the said flowing water. The phenomenon was incorrectly interpreted until Einstein appeared on the scene.

The experiment repeated with benzine, in which the speed of light is even less than in water (124,000 m/s), gave the following results: Benzine moving with a speed of 31 m/s plus light moving with a speed of 124,000 m/s equals light reaching 124,017 m/s (and not 124,031 m/s), according to classical mechanics.

The law of the addition of speeds ($v + v' = v''$) was proved wrong, and Einstein showed that the correct formula derived once more from the Lorentz transformation in the shape of this equation:

$$v'' = \frac{v + v'}{1 + \dfrac{vv'}{c^2}}$$

Just as the experiments of Michelson, Morley, and Miller had suggested to Einstein the postulate of a constancy of the velocity of light in space, a maximum unsurpassable in nature (c), the natural radioactivity revealed by Becquerel and subsequently by Pierre and Marie Curie, which implied the caducity of the principle of the indestructibility of matter, since the latter emitted radiation, so that a part of its mass became transformed into pure energy, led him to the conclusion that mass and energy were one. The Frenchman Lebon had already suspected this identity, but he had not quantified it, and Einstein was the first not only to maintain that matter was "a reservoir of energy" (mass is concentrated energy) but also to establish the famous equation $E = mc^2$, i.e. E the energy (in the original formula this E was replaced by W) = the mass (m), multiplied by the velocity of light squared (c^2), the corollary of which is naturally: $m = \dfrac{E}{c^2}$, i.e. mass is equal to energy divided by the speed of light squared.

Numerous experiments prior to the discovery of radioactivity gave support to the argument of the pioneers in this new field. Prout's hypothesis, which led to the admission that an atom of any matter is only a conglomeration of hydrogen atoms (which we know today to be true, or at least that every proton is a nucleus of the hydrogen atom, a fact that illustrates to perfection the unity to be found in nature), was seriously compromised by the fact that "atomic weights" did not turn out to be whole multiples of the hydrogen atom. Without entering into the extremely complicated details of the structure of atoms,* we shall merely say that the synthesis of the heavy nuclei is accompanied by an emission of energy (like a chemical reaction—in other words, a synthesis of atoms in molecules is accompanied by a far less important emission of energy), and that the loss of mass of a nuclear complex in relation to the mass of the far simpler nucleus of the hydrogen atom is the equivalent of this energy. To sum up, the mass of individual protons (and neutrons) is $\dfrac{E}{c^2}$

---

* For further details, cf. the work of the author: *L'énergie nucléaire* (Correa) or his pamphlet: *L'Atome* in *L'Encyclopédie des Sciences et des Techniques* (Edition Lidis).

less when they are agglomerated than would be the case if these particles were weighed separately.

Einstein established his formula purely by logic. It was later proved by experiment, and it is for this reason that we speak of Einstein's genius, or rather of his brilliant intuition.

The relationship Einstein saw between mass and energy led to research into the liberation of nuclear energy in all its forms (fission in the notorious atom bomb and the reactors, fusion in the no less notorious H-bomb).

From this point we could understand why the sun could radiate at the loss of so little mass; the speed of light is a very large denominator, and when we take its square (c^2), the formula establishes that a small quantity of mass is transformed into a very large quantity of energy (the thermonuclear reactions that take place in the stars are furthermore due to an economic cycle leading to the transformation of protons or nuclei of the hydrogen atom into nuclei of the helium atom or alpha particles).

Solar radiation represents a loss of mass of four million tons per second which is distributed in space, a very small part of which we receive on our earth, and by which our globe must "become constantly heavier." It undoubtedly does "grow heavier," but the transfer of solar energy is compensated for on the one hand by reflection and on the other hand by the loss of energy due to physico-chemical processes. These processes take place both in the organic and inorganic fields so that one can presume that a constant interchange exists between the microcosm and the macrocosm.

That man did not previously perceive that energy has "weight" was on account of the weakness of our methods of measurement, but all increase of energy leads to an increase of mass (just as all loss of energy leads to a decrease of mass). We know, for example, today that a quart of water that rises in temperature from 0° to 100° centigrade is slightly heavier. But the phenomenon is imperceptible in practice, since it is a question of an increase of mass of the order of only one fifth of a billionth of a gram. A gram represents an energy of twenty-five million kilowatt hours. . . .

To sum up, relativity shows that all energy is massive—heat and visible or invisible light. Now it is thanks to a transfer of energy that it is possible, as we have already seen, to overcome inertia, the concomitant of all mass, i.e. that we need energy both to set in motion a motionless body and to accelerate an object in movement (let us recall that mass is the inertia of a certain quantity of energy). Quite naturally, this energy necessary to displace a mass has to be added to the said mass, just as this mass, by increasing, increases its inertia, and it thus becomes more and more difficult to accelerate, i.e. in order to increase the speed of a moving body going faster and faster, more and more energy is needed. Laplace could not have put it better.

But what Laplace could not have foreseen is that by reason of the limitation of velocity in the universe (186,000 m/s, the speed of light in space) the possibility of adding velocities according to classical mechanics is no longer permitted, and this precisely by reason of the increase of mass (and of its inertia) which would become infinite (i.e. when inertia would totally oppose any augmentation of the speed of movement) if the speed of light (c) could be reached.

If m_0 is the mass at rest (or more accurately, the mass taken as such) in a given system, according to Einstein, a body launched with the velocity v in this system acquires a mass (m) in accordance with the following equation:

$$m = \frac{m_0}{\sqrt{1 - \dfrac{v^2}{c^2}}}$$

It was once more the study of the particles of cosmic radiation, accelerated to the point where they almost reached the velocity of light, which provided the first experimental proof. It was observed that the mass of these particles could increase to 40,000 times more than when at rest. In the great accelerators one can observe an increase in mass of 5 to 10 percent at a speed of more than 124,000 m/s. Under a tension of twenty-five billion volts in the synchro-phasotron of the C.E.R.N.* at Geneva, where the accelerated particles can reach 99.94 percent of the velocity of light, the mass is multiplied by twenty-six. As one approached c, according to the classical formula of kinetic energy $\frac{1}{2}mv^2$, the speed increases less and

* Centre Européen de Recherches Nucléaires.

less while the mass increases more and more: energy acts more on m than on v.

In short the equation that gives the true mass of a particle in movement and affords a subsidiary proof that it is impossible to achieve the velocity of light, when this mass would become infinite, is as follows:

$$E = \frac{m_0\, c^2}{\sqrt{1 - \dfrac{v^2}{c^2}}}$$

The identity of mass and energy is spectacularly proved by the creation of matter (electrons in a simple cyclotron; nuclei in the great accelerators), but we must point out here that by reason of the law of conservation of charge it is only possible for twin particles of contrary electric signs to be created—an electron and a positron, a proton and an antiproton, a neutron and an antineutron (differentiated only by their spins or magnetic moments, since a neutron—electrically neutral, as its name implies—integrates the two charges).

This is how the operation is realized: hydrogen nuclei, protons previously ionized, are accelerated until they reach as nearly as possible the velocity of light, in a vacuum as perfect as it is possible to obtain (but which still falls far short of the interplanetary pseudo-void). This takes place in a circular metal tube, naturally airtight, held between the jaws of giant electromagnets. When it is no longer possible to accelerate the particles any further, a target of matter, possibly paraffin, intercepts them.

In theory any material could be used, since it is a question of making one of the nuclei strike one of the atoms, a component of this matter. A "shock" is naturally produced, or more accurately an "elastic shock," from which new particles are born spontaneously.

The particles are not actually born from the shock, but form from the energy dissipated during the shock: *the collision is the catalyst inducing a production of matter.*

The best proof is that much more energy is needed to create a pair of nuclei, since this total mass is represented by the formula:

$$m = \frac{E}{c^2}$$

In order to create a pair of electrons, a feat that was already accomplished in cyclotrons long before the war, an energy equivalent to one million volts would suffice (500,000 for the positron and 500,000 for the negative electron). But a nucleus *en gros* attains a mass representing 1,840 times that of an electron. In theory, therefore, it would need slightly less than a billion volts per nucleus, or nearly two billion volts for the effective creation of matter in the form of two particles, the one being the "anti" of the other from the electromagnetic point of view.

We have seen, however, that the impact provokes an "elastic shock." The energy dissipated will therefore be only half that used for the acceleration, which means at a first approximation that four instead of two billion volts will be needed for the creation of a pair of nuclei. And this is not all. We are now sufficiently familiar with this problem to avoid the necessity of repeating that more accelerating energy is needed as the mass increases, and that this increase is relative to the speed previously given to the particle.

Without going into technical details and complicated calculations it can be said that in order to obtain two particles intrinsically demanding an energy corresponding to their mass, approximately two billion volts, three times greater energy has to be employed—in other words, six billion volts and even a little more.

It was on this account that the great accelerators of particles were built. The Bevatron, at the University of California at Berkeley, only just had this capacity (6.2 billion volts), and it was there that they were able to announce for the first time, in 1956, the creation of matter and antimatter.

As soon as they appear the antiprotons and the antineutrons (in the same way as the positrons) are destroyed on meeting their "natural" homologs (from the terrestrial point of view protons, neutrons—and electrons). As a result they liberate the energy with which they had been built. We are then faced with new phenomena of the materialization of nuclear and electromagnetic fields—in other words, with a cascading production of mesons and photons.

The creation of matter and antimatter has also been observed with the synchro-phasotron at Dubna,* with its power of ten billion volts. The proton synchrotrons of C.E.R.N. at Geneva and of Bevatron in the United States, with their respective power of twenty-five and twenty-six billion volts, are needed to obtain the foreign (nonbasic particles) known as hyperons, whose mass exceeds that of nuclei.

* Dubna Research Laboratories for Nuclear Physics in the U.S.S.R.

3

The Life of Einstein

ALBERT EINSTEIN was a man of wide culture. The classic
figures of theoretical physics held no secrets for him—in particular, Helmholtz, Kirchhoff, Maxwell, and Hertz. In mathematics he favored Henri Poincaré, Lorentz, Gauss, and
Riemann. His basic philosophy was that of Kant, David
Hume, and above all of Ernst Mach.

Admittedly, he studied the writings of Schopenhauer and
Nietzsche, but, to quote his own words, he read them for his
own "edification," and according to Franck, "without taking
any of their views seriously."

He himself was a philosopher in the true meaning of the
word, that is to say, a man "interested in nature," whom the
ancient Greeks would have called a physiologist. He considered himself in this light.

According to Leopold Infeld, his philosophy was based on
the idea that none of the questions concerning the existence
and nature of our external world are meaningless and that, on
the contrary, it is possible to give a meaning "being" and
"nonbeing."

"I asked him one day," said Infeld, " 'Is there any reality
apart from ourselves?' "

" 'Yes,' " replied Einstein. " 'I really believe it.' "

Traditional philosophy, according to Infeld, remains in
substance speculative. Its adepts use complicated words and
long phrases which are a closed book to the ordinary man.
They discuss intuition, imagination, the "thing in itself," trying

to arrive at an impossible synthesis between faith and experience. Such considerations are out of date: all the problems of the universe are absorbed by physics, mathematics, biology, and psychology. A philosopher in the modern sense is a man interested in the data of our knowledge and one who tries to clarify basic concepts. Einstein must be numbered among them.

Einstein has alternatively been considered as a materialist and an idealist. He has been incorporated into all manner of schools—positivists, empiricists, etc. Some have spoken of relativity as a logical abstraction, devoid of all reality, while others saw in it a new metaphysics (Einstein once remarked that there was a metaphysical content in all physics).

"Since the positivist conception of physics had been greatly stimulated by the work of Einstein, the pioneer of relativity and atomism," writes Philipp Franck, "many people looked upon him as a kind of patron saint of positivism. To the positivists he seemed to bring the blessing of science: to their adversaries he was an evil genius. In actual fact his attitude toward positivism and metaphysics was not so simple. . . . Einstein recognized unreservedly Niels Bohr's great success in explaining numerous phenomena of atomic physics, but from the philosophical point of view he was not prepared to admit that one should abandon the goal of a description of physical reality and merely be content with collecting observations."

Einstein, who took a great deal from Mach, rejected the latter's positivist theories. He shared the ideas of Planck, according to whom physical laws described a reality in space and time—a reality independent of ourselves.

Einstein never saw anything metaphysical, as the term is generally understood in the relativist theories. He clearly stated that he considered an electromagnetic or gravitational field as a physical reality in the same context as matter is considered: "Relativity," he said, "teaches us the connection between the different descriptions of one and the same reality."

On the other hand he was never prepared to accept that there was a cast-iron framework for physics. He claimed the right to create a system of formulae and laws in accord with the observations. We quote Franck once more: "For Einstein the fundamental theoretical laws are a free creation of the imagination, the product of the activity of an inventor whose speculations are limited by two principles: one empirical, according to which the conclusions drawn from the theory must be confirmed by experience, and a semilogical, semi-aesthetic principle according to which the fundamental laws should be as few as possible and compatible with logic."

A well-known Marxist, Walter Hollitscher, wrote for his part: "Subjectivists and relativists have tried to use the theories of Albert Einstein to give a modern varnish to the experience of the outside world and its 'unknowability.' The stalwart champions of mechanistic metaphysical materialism believed it their duty to oppose the theory of relativity because it did not correspond to their preconceived scheme of the immutable relations of space and time detached from matter. . . . This detracted from the main idea according to which the relativity theory teaches the indissoluble relativity of matter and movement in its space-time coordinates. Basic relativity in the domain of physics and space-time determinations of matter (in the sense of the relativity theory), do not at all conflict with the epistemology according to which man by his relative knowledge continually approaches absolute truth, and the ultimate comprehension of truth. This approach is an infinite process which, each time it reaches the goal fixed, immediately takes a more elevated objective. The relativity theory does not deny reality as the goal of absolute knowledge, it only denies the existence of physical systems 'in absolute rest' and in consequence the existence of 'systems of absolute reference.' "

For us scientific materialists, the relativity theory—and in this it is unique—also represents reality. No one is capable of representing a "four-dimensional space" in concrete form. The latter can be defined only by mathematical abstraction, but it is not for this reason incorporated in metaphysics. Since the universe is not static but, on the contrary, essentially dynamic, no static image, no snapshot, even though purporting to be instantaneous, can give us a correct interpretation, and the parameter of time is indispensable in the representation of a space-time continuum, the sole reality.

Given the finite character of the velocity of light which implies the relativity of simultaneity, everything instantaneous or pseudo-instantaneous is a dangerous illusion. A photographic snapshot can effectively represent a spatial event in time with an adequate space-time approximation (in fact absolute or quasi-absolute) if the depth of the field of the shot is very limited in terrestrial space, because the relativity of simultaneity is not appreciable on this scale (we could say that we see *simultaneously* the clock on a station platform and the train leaving 35 feet away from it).

But already, as far as a sunset is concerned, we are forced to admit that it is not quite the same, because there is a lag of more than eight minutes (about 500 seconds at 186,000 m/s for the approximate 93,000,000 miles, the average distance of the sun from the earth) between the departure of the rays of light and the moment when they strike our watch dial or when we snap the shutter of our camera.

But this is nothing compared with the error of the effect of perspective of stellar constellations whose distribution in space, because of their very different distance "in depth," makes us photograph stars forming these constellations in an identical earth time, whereas the luminous rays recorded on our photographic plate differ vastly in age—by dozens, hundreds, and thousands of years. . . .

We know in fact that the nearest star to us is about four light years away, in other words about 23.5 trillion miles; if this star exploded at some moment of our earth time, we should only learn about it four years later by this same earth time. Conversely, we could quite well have photographed the ghosts ·of stars which disappeared a century or perhaps a thousand years ago. . . .

Time as a fourth dimension often comes into our representation of a terrestrial event, since, not content with signaling the exact spot where a particular incident took place, we are obliged if we wish to be precise, to state what day and at what hour this event took place. In relativity we merely use an identical proposition (time is always a supplementary coordinate of the space coordinates). But our measurements of time and space are essentially subordinate to rays of light (they indicate to us the intervals of space between one object and another as well as intervals of time, i.e. they give us the speed of movement of these objects in space in relation to each other). We know, however, that light is not propagated instantaneously but at a limited velocity (relativity of simultaneity, which implies the shrinking of the measuring rods and the slowing down of the clock progressively as the speed of the moving objects, in relation to the observer, considered at rest, approaches that of light). A photograph taken of the sky on a beautiful summer night by no means represents reality unless we specify that it has to be translated into space-time.

The assertion that the speed of light is limited is neither a convention nor an arbitrary subjective. It is a certified statement, and the theory of relativity, supported by incontestable experiments, as we saw in the preceding chapter, shows that if the speed of 186,000 m/s could be achieved all length would be reduced to zero, every clock would stop and every mass would increase indefinitely—in other words, to the point where, conforming to the principle of the identity of weight and inert mass, it would be impossible to increase the speed of a body.

It serves no useful purpose, as certain people have maintained, to object that, all speed being relative, light itself perforce also being relative, the relativist effects are only mathematical tricks of a purely theoretical value. Merely to quote once more the example most difficult to admit by the uninitiated, that of "Langevin's traveler," it appears beyond doubt that if relative to his personal clock, his time did not seem to him to be distended (i.e. that his biological rhythms, relative to his personal clock, remained identical to what they were on earth) relative to the earth dwellers who would see him leave and return at a speed approaching that of light, this time will have been effectively slowed down: two of his years will represent for them approximately two centuries, as we have already indicated in a previous chapter.

It is unthinkable that physics will ever bring back a conception of absolute time and absolute space, and all relativist philosophy agrees upon this *a priori*.

DURING THE FIRST WORLD WAR

After being appointed university lecturer at Berne—the publication of his first theories had drawn attention to him, and his job in the Patent Office was no longer compatible with his new status—Einstein was awarded the Chair of Physics at Zürich Polytechnic. Later, at the end of 1910, he was appointed Professor to Prague University by decree of the Austrian Emperor, Franz Joseph.

It was at Zürich, and later at Prague, that he elaborated and finally completed the special theory of relativity, although it had already existed in its broader outlines since 1905. In 1911 he tackled the *generalization* of relativity with a work entitled: *Über den Einfluss der Schwerkraft auf die Ausbreitung des Lichtes* (The Influence of Gravitation on the Propagation of Light).

In 1913, having resigned his professorship at Prague, where university conflicts (Germans versus Czechs, Czechs versus Jews, and Germans and Czechs united in anti-Semitism) often placed this man, who had repudiated all nationality and religion, in an insupportable position, Einstein returned to Zürich. Since his married life with Mileva was on the verge of collapse he received with a certain amount of pleasure two illustrious envoys from the German Emperor William II, the physicists Max Planck and Walter Nernst, who had come to offer him the directorship of the research organization for theoretical physics in Germany. If he accepted he would become in addition a member of the Prussian Academy of Sciences and professor at Berlin University, and he was not asked to renew German nationality.

Naturally it was a brilliant offer from the financial as well as the honorific points of view, but Einstein never cared for honors, and the reason he accepted was primarily because it gave him an excellent opportunity for separating from Mileva, who was quite agreeable to this arrangement.

Thus we have Einstein, the notorious antimilitarist, on the eve of war in the most military country in the world. Do not let us make the common mistake that Germany at that time was the only one who wanted war, for the French "seekers of revenge" did nothing to prevent the spread of the conflict; it is a fact, however, that the German people were even more misguided than the French. Even in the highest intellectual circles an exaggerated nationalism was the order of the day. The famous "manifesto of '93," justifiably qualified by Einstein as "the capitulation of German intellectual independence" is a proof of this. Einstein himself had naturally refused categorically to sign the manifesto, and only his fame and his qualification as a neutral saved him from popular reprisals and university persecution.

But from now onward he was an isolated figure. When he

At the age of twenty-six, in Berne (1905)

Giving a demonstration

took his chair at the academy, which he did less and less often, the two seats at his side remained ostentatiously empty.

"Will future generations," he wrote sadly to Romain Rolland, exiled to Switzerland by the French, "really be able to glorify our Europe where three centuries of the most intensive cultural work have ended in nothing more than a change from religious to nationalist mania. Even the scholars here and in France behave as though their brains have been amputated."

Signing countermanifestoes, speaking at certain illegal pacifist manifestations, making contact with colleagues whom he considered not too tainted by "war madness," he was under no illusion as to his action. "Many people don't like it," he said with a sigh, "but they remain passive because they're scared of the others."

A NEW FAMILY LIFE

In Berlin, Einstein lived almost permanently with an uncle whose daughter, neither particularly young nor pretty and without a trace of coquetry, attracted him because of her sweetness and sound common sense. She was able to isolate him from the world, which had become too importunate, and to safeguard his peace and serenity. He married her.

Frau Elsa was vivacious and amiable. She had two daughters, and Einstein, whose health gave rise to anxiety, found himself in the bosom of a real family. At this time there was a food shortage, but Elsa worked wonders to see that "her" Albert lacked for nothing. She understood very little about his work, but she was fully conscious of his genius.

"People keep talking about what you are working on at the moment," she said to him one day. "Everyone asks me for news, and I really appear too stupid when I say that I know nothing. Couldn't you tell me what it's all about?"

"Well," replied Einstein after a moment's hesitation, "next time they ask you, you just say that you know everything, but you can't speak about it because it's a great secret."

He beamed with delight at this invention. All those who met him recall with pleasure this charming side of his character: a childish side ready to enjoy trifles provided they were not vulgar, and a constantly renewed capacity for wonder at the splendor of natural phenomena, which matched the depth of his thought. Few men have been privileged to detach themselves to such an extent from the tiresome details of everyday life—few men of science and very few philosophers. Hence the solitude in which he lived in the midst of academic circles.

He did not like discussing the current problems of professional life. He never took them seriously. Franck recalls: "The daily life of a university often leads to discussion. People worry about the frequency at which works should be published, about colleagues who have or have not published anything, about a colleague who too often or perhaps not often enough quotes another colleague or who has failed intentionally or unintentionally to quote someone else. There are debates on the merits of certain professors, on the honors they hold or have not been awarded by their university or other universities, on the academies to which they have or have not been elected. The conversation turns to the number of students whom the professors have been able to provide with a post; to students and masters who have been capable of preventing them from finding posts; to the question of knowing if they have any influence on their superiors or if they are capable of obtaining money from the authorities for their department."

All this irritated Einstein, and he let it be seen sometimes to the point of rudeness. Questions of precedence interested him as little as the problems of finance. His needs were very few, for his whole world was inside him, radiating toward the cosmos, delving in the microcosm and submerged in the macrocosm. He refused to take even a semblance of interest in all this pettiness.

He was extraordinarily patient with students and with amateurs. He always tried to explain to them in simple words and in a few lucid phrases the essentials of the questions that troubled them. "I am always prepared to receive you," he said to his pupils; "if you have a problem, bring it to me at once; you will never disturb me because I can interrupt my work at any minute and take it up again after the interruption."

Whereas so many people take a pride in never having any time, it was Einstein's boast, according to Franck, that he always had time. "I remember a visit during the course of which we decided to go together on a visit to the Potsdam Observatory. We had agreed to meet at a certain spot, but since I did not know Berlin I said that I might not be punctual at the rendezvous."

"Oh, that won't matter," replied Einstein. "I'll wait for you on the bridge."

"But I don't want to waste your time," protested Franck.

"You won't," replied Einstein. "My type of work can be done anywhere. Why should I meditate on my problems any better at home than on the bridge at Potsdam?"

"This was typical of Einstein," concludes Franck. "His thoughts flowed like a constant stream. Each conversation that interrupted its course was like a pebble thrown into a powerful river, quite incapable of disturbing its progress."

Einstein was full of mischievous humor, and even Elsa did not escape his teasing: "When women are at home," he said, "they spend all the time on their furniture. They hover around all day and are always causing trouble about it. When I travel with my wife I am the only piece of furniture she has to hand, and then she cannot prevent hovering around me and finding something to tidy all day long."

It was Elsa who kept the visitors at bay. She was ruthless in showing the door to the importunate. Einstein, however, was not the man to let himself be influenced in the matter of his friends, and she bowed to his orders while deploring that he often let himself be badgered by people whom, as a result of her bourgeois upbringing, she considered of little importance. But for Einstein there were no systematic divisions between men: "I do not find class differences justified," he said. "I think they are established by violence." He had a profound respect for manual work and often said that every scientist should be a cobbler so that he would have plenty of time to think.

4

The General Theory of Relativity

EINSTEIN'S theories completely upset previously held ideas. Today the special theory of relativity has been universally accepted—although there is still controversy with regard to its philosophical interpretation—but at the beginning of the present century, when conservatism ruled, his theories clashed not only with university practice but also with "common sense."

It was difficult to imagine that time did not pass uniformly as had been accepted for centuries. People also found it difficult to understand the negation of the ether, without which it seemed that the transmission of electromagnetic waves was "impossible." People found it hard to conceive that space before containing this hypothetical ether had no true existence. It was doubted whether energy could transform itself into matter and vice versa.

Einstein calmly, and sometimes mischievously, let his critics talk and kept quiet. He knew how to hold on to the truth, although he always declared expressly that one day relativity would undergo the fate of Newtonian gravitation with regard to the still unobservable portions of our universe; in other words, that it would then only be valid as "a first approximation," and that new evidence of vaster laws would transcend into relativist principles.

But there were still to be many surprises in store for the world. In 1905 Max Born had written, "In my view one of the most remarkable works in the whole of scientific literature

69

has been published this year in *Annalen der Physik,* on the subject of relativity."

The second phase of Einstein's work began in 1911, and, as we have seen, it brought him world fame.

In the special theory Einstein had studied the phenomenon of movement. He had shown that in the universe no general standards of time or space exist by which it is possible to show the absolute movement of the earth or any other system: these movements exist only *relatively* to other systems, which are themselves in movement. If all the bodies that people the universe suddenly disappeared with a single exception, those who lived on the solitary object would, according to the special theory, have no means of knowing whether that object was in movement or at rest.

Nevertheless, Einstein wondered if there were not certain cases in which movement could be revealed by some physical phenomenon, caused by a movement without reference to another system (in movement or considered as at rest).

Here is another example taken from a railway. Everyone has undergone this relativist experience. In a station where two trains stand next to each other waiting to leave, the traveler in his seat has often remarked that the adjacent train suddenly starts to file slowly past his own window. He has often wondered whether it was his own train or the neighboring train that was "moving." He could obtain no satisfactory reply to this question except by looking at the platform or, better still, at some pillar standing on this platform. If this pillar was not "moving" (relative to his carriage window), there was no doubt that the movement came from the other train. If on the other hand the pillar seemed to move, he could deduce that his own train was under way.

Departures of course do not always take place so quietly. Sometimes the engineer sets off violently or after a slow departure sharply applies his brakes. As a result of the ensuing shock the traveler is aware of a change of acceleration and more particularly in the second instance of a change of speed. He has no need therefore of a relativist comparison to know that he is moving.

It seems possible, therefore, thought Einstein, to discern an *absolute movement* (no longer "relative to something") from phenomena identical to those which occur to travelers by train —phenomena which disturb his comfort, either by thrusting him back in his seat or jolting him forward or, when the train takes a bend too fast, flinging him to right or left according to the direction of the turn.

It would seem, he thought, that if the earth was alone in a pseudo-space, there would be nothing to indicate that it was motionless or, on the contrary, animated by a uniform movement; *nothing except in the case when there was a change or "acceleration"*: energy capable of overcoming inertia, acceleration, deceleration, centrifugal force.

In the special theory of relativity Einstein had shown that movement can only be relative. Now on the basis of these new reflections everything led him to suppose that a nonuniform movement such as that produced by forces or acceleration could be *absolute*. Did this not seem to suggest that space could serve as an inner system of reference from which it was possible to distinguish an absolute movement? Such a contradiction disturbed him deeply. His profound conviction was that the laws of nature must be the same for all systems, independent of their movements.

Taking as the basis of his new reasoning the Galilean-Newtonian law of inertia: *"Every body remains motionless or continues in uniform movement, unless this state is modified by forces exerted on it,"* he came to the conclusion that it was *inertia* which produces the particular sensations experienced by the traveler when a train puts on speed, slows down, or enters a bend. Everything encourages the mass of the travelers' body to continue moving in a straight line: *inertia resists the force that tends to impose upon it a change of speed or direction.*

Inertia demands a different energy according to the difference of the masses to be moved or halted. The more considerable the mass the greater will be the energy demanded, and in consequence the greater the inertia of this mass. Newton had already demonstrated this, and everybody knows it more or less intuitively. *"The quantity of force necessary to accelerate a body, according to Newton, depends on the mass of that body: If the same force is applied to two bodies of different masses, it produces a greater acceleration on the smaller body."*

After Galileo's experiments from the Leaning Tower of Pisa it was logical to admit that a particular situation exists where there seems to be no relation between the acceleration of a body and its mass. Repeated in the vacuum or pseudo-vacuum of a laboratory tube, these experiments prove that on earth all bodies "fall" at exactly the same speed whatever their dimensions, compositions, and masses; a feather and a piece of lead leaving at the same time from the top of the tube reach the bottom in strictly identical time (in the air it is the atmospheric density that acts as a brake on the feather). Newton proved that the phenomenon was due to the earth's attraction, in other words that it corresponded to the laws of universal gravity, of which the attraction of the earth is only one particular instance. Everything transpires, he announced, as though the masses attracted each other reciprocally *in the ratio of these masses and the inverse ratio of the square of the distance separating them*" (from center to center of these masses). The larger the object, the stronger the attraction of gravity: if the object is small its inertia (or tendency to resist movement) is equally small, but since the attraction of gravity is then small what is called "specific gravity" is strictly the same for the small and the large object.

This "remarkable" coincidence had never been explained until Einstein. It was stated and accepted, considered in fact as a "lucky chance." But Einstein was not satisfied. He found it odd that the equivalence of gravity and inertia should be "an accident of nature."

We know that Newton never quite accepted the idea of a "mysterious force," implied by gravitation, and that from scruple he prefaced his enunciations with this cautious phrase: "Everything happens as though . . ." Einstein went further. He categorically rejected the idea that gravitation is a force that can be exercised instantaneously along great distances: this "instantaneous" propagation being already in contradiction to the postulate of the special relativity theory according to which the velocity of light cannot be exceeded.

Einstein always loved simple examples, pictures that one might sometimes have considered with suspicion on account of their naïveté; for example, of trains, boxes, rooms, and elevators. He imagined that in a gigantic skyscraper an elevator containing intrepid physicists accidentally became detached from its cable and fell freely. These physicists calmly took from their pockets all kinds of objects—pens, keys, and coins—and, opening their palms, could observe that these objects no longer fell toward the floor of the elevator, but kept in balance as they themselves were, that is to say, in the exact situation that would have been theirs had they found themselves in space, far from any field of gravitation instead of in a free-falling elevator. . . .

If they were suddenly struck with amnesia, our physicists would not know whether they were falling in a gravitational field or floating in empty space. Now, using his discretionary power, Einstein magically transported the elevator into galactic space—that is to say, far from any field of gravitation. The elevator obeyed the Galilean-Newtonian law of inertia, i.e. that its occupants could either consider that they were in a state of rest or that the elevator pursued a uniform linear movement. The effect was strictly the same for them, and they had no possibility for verification. In any case everything transpired as though they were at rest, far removed from any gravitational field, and the ideas of "up" or "down" had no further significance for them. They could just as well with a muscular effort walk on the floor, on the ceiling, or on the walls of their car. Furthermore, if with another wave of the magic wand, we transformed our elevator into a cubic box, whose walls had no landmarks, it became quite absurd to speak of a ceiling, a floor, or anything else. . . .

For our convenience let us retain the picture of the elevator. Einstein, always an imaginative thinker, attached a cable to the roof of the elevator (i.e. by the external hook above the roof); he next imagined that a kind of superman pulled on the cable, the effect of which was to displace the car at a constant acceleration.

What are the physicists, who have noticed nothing and who cannot imagine the presence of this superman towing them, now going to think? Some summary experiences will quite naturally be in store for them. First, they will observe that they once more have "weight," and that they can now keep a grip on the floor of the car as on terra firma. If they now drop their keys, pens, or other objects, they will fall once more. They can therefore logically admit that *they are in a field of gravitation.* If the acceleration of the elevator is now maintained at about 10 m/s, they will have the impression of really being on earth or on some planet with the same mass as that of the earth. (If the acceleration decreased and in consequence they felt "lighter," they might imagine, for example, that they were on the moon; if on the other hand it increased and they felt "heavier" to the point where this "weight" became unbearable, they might imagine that they were on Jupiter, etc.)

They would also have a glimpse of reality—i.e. they would notice that they were moving in space with a constant acceleration. . . .

If, now, instead of pulling continuously on the cable outside the cabin, our superman turned it on his extended arm like a leaf, bringing about the effect that is known as "centrifugal force," our "guinea pigs" would no longer be aware of the change. They could still think that they were at rest in a gravitational field or, on the contrary, that they were in accelerated rectilinear movement somewhere in space without other requisite conditions.

From these fantasies of his imagination Albert Einstein drew his *Principle of the Equivalence of Gravitation and Inertia.* The latter establishes very simply that there is no means of distinguishing between the movement produced by the forces of inertia (acceleration, recoil, centrifugal force, etc.) and the movement produced by the "force of gravity."

This principle is the touchstone of the general relativity theory. It provides the answer to both the enigma of gravity and to the problem of absolute movement. It demonstrates that there is nothing unique or absolute in nonuniform movement, *for the effects of this nonuniform movement, which could, one imagines, reveal the state of movement of a body, even if it were alone in space, cannot be distinguished from the effects of gravity.*

Every effort of inertia, produced by a change of speed or a change of direction, can be attributed equally to a change or to a variation of the gravitational field.

The basic premises of relativity remained true: *movement, whether uniform or nonuniform, can be judged only in relation to a frame of reference: there is no such thing as absolute movement.*

The consequence of this postulate was extremely important since it led to the idea of the sole reality of fields.

"The law of universal gravity," Einstein points out, *"describes the behavior of objects in a gravitational field, not in terms of attraction, but simply in terms describing the paths*

followed by these objects." The gravitational laws within the framework of the general relativity theory translate the inertia of matter: the movements of objects that punctuate space (stars, planets, galaxies, comets, meteorites, etc.) *are born of their inherent inertia,* and the path they follow is determined by the metric properties of space, or rather from the metric properties of the space-time continuum.

Just as Faraday and Maxwell demonstrated that a magnet creates certain properties of the space surrounding it (an electromagnetic field that can be demonstrated by powdering a sheet of paper held above a magnet with filings), Einstein postulated that the stars, the planets—in fact, all material bodies—determine individually the properties of the space surrounding them. Just as in a magnetic field the movement of a bar of iron is determined by the structure of the magnetic field, in a gravitational field the path of any body is determined by the (space-time) geometry of this gravitational field.

On this subject Einstein states: *"In the general theory of relativity, the doctrine of space and time, kinematics is no longer one of the absolute bases of general physics. The geometric properties of bodies and the rhythms of clocks depend in the first analysis on their gravitational fields which, in turn, are produced by the particular system."*

Let us examine this a little more closely. Here, according to Einstein, we have a space-time domain in which there exists no field of gravitation relative to a frame of reference K, whose state of movement has been conveniently chosen. In relation to the domain under review K is therefore a Galilean frame of reference, and the findings of the special theory are valid with regard to it.

Let us suppose that the same domain is referred to a second frame of reference K', which is animated by a uniform rotating movement in relation to K.

Einstein proposes to represent K' by a circular disc carrying out a uniform rotating movement in its plane around its center.

"An observer," he says, "sits on the periphery of the disc (K'). This observer is subjected to a force which acts in the radial direction outward, and which is interpreted as an effect of inertia (centrifugal force) by an observer who is at rest in relation to the first frame of reference (K). (If we imagine ourselves to be these observers on the earth considered at rest, we fulfill the conditions of K. The disc K' can then be conceived as a spatial platform freed of all specific gravity.)"

But conforming to the above-mentioned postulates of relativity (the analogy between specific gravity, centrifugal force, acceleration, etc.), this observer (K') can quite well consider his disc as motionless in a gravitational field (he is the inhabitant of the immense spatial platform).

Wishing to obtain indications of the time and space with regard to his disc, the observer K' places two clocks of the same construction, one at the center of the disc and the second at its periphery, so that these clocks are at rest relative to the disc.

We must first ask ourselves, says Einstein, if these two clocks have the same speed, from the point of view of the Galilean frame of reference K, not animated by a rotating movement? No, for in relation to the latter the clock situated at the center has no speed, whereas the clock placed at the periphery is in movement because of the rotation of the disc.

According to the principle of the slowing down of the clocks in the special relativity theory, the clock at the periphery will be slow (the conclusion of the observer K) on the one hand in relation to his own clock, and on the other hand in relation to the clock placed at the center of the disc.

It is obvious that the observer K', placed at the center of his disc, will observe the same difference as K between the time recorded by the periphery clock and that shown by the central clock (apart from a slight lag on the dial from the Einsteinian effect, but let us not go into details).

"In every field of gravitation," Einstein concludes, "a clock will in consequence gain or lose according to the position it occupies (at rest). It is therefore impossible to give a reasonable definition of time by means of clocks, which are at rest in relation to the frames of reference; for we come up against a similar difficulty when we attempt to apply here our former definition of simultaneity."

In fact, as far as these space coordinates are concerned, if the observer in movement with the disc (K') places his measuring rod (which, Einstein stresses, is small in relation to the radius of the disc) at a tangent to the periphery of the latter, its length *in relation to the observer* K *of the Galilean system* will be less than 1, since again according to the special theory of relativity previously explained, with regard to the contraction of space, bodies in movement undergo a shortening in the direction of their movement.

If the observer K' (the one on the disc) places his measuring rod in the direction of the radius of the disc, this rod in relation to the observer K (Galilean) will undergo no shortening. This means, briefly, that when K' wants to calculate the area of the disc by measuring, as is logical, the circumference and its diameter and then dividing the results, he will not find his quotient to be 3.1416 (π) but a higher figure (K will naturally find π).

Thus, according to Einstein it is proved that the propositions of Euclidian geometry cannot be strictly true in a gravitational field, when we give the rod the length 1 at all loci and in all directions: *the idea of the straight line in consequence loses its significance.* We are no longer in a position to define accurately, in our example of the disc and in relation to this disc, the coordinates x, y, z, according to the methods used in the special relativity theory. *Inasmuch as the coordinates and times of the events are not defined, the laws of nature in which they meet have no precise meaning.* [Our italics.]

This implies that, for a correct definition of cosmic events, Euclidian geometry must be abandoned in favor of a new geometry, the existence of which had been foreseen by Lobatchevski and Gauss and formulated by Riemann. These were the authors whom Einstein consulted in the main.

THE SPACE-TIME CONTINUUM

Before approaching the idea of the curvature of space as understood in the general theory of relativity—the curve resulting from the abandonment of the Euclidian space-time continuum satisfying the special theory—in favor of non-Euclidian continua (Riemannian space) which, as we have just seen, the general relativity theory demands, we must define the nature of a space-time continuum. We shall then see how Einstein demonstrated that a ray of light, pure energy, could be curved in a gravitational field, a fact that attacked the principle of the invariance postulated by the special theory of relativity.

It is the "specific gravity" of light (the equivalence of

mass and energy) which determines the curvature of space-time. The curve of the light ray represents a contraction of the measuring rods and the clocks, itself determined by the gravitational effect (just as relative velocity determines an identical effect of the shortening of the rods and the slowing down of the clocks). The universe appears in time and space as a space-time continuum curved by reason of the masses it contains: the rays of light issuing from a source are gradually curved, deviated in the course of their journey, and however slight this curve may be, it will, according to Einstein, ultimately "enclose" the universe on itself.

Let us recall that Minkowsky, Einstein's teacher at Zürich University, was the first to put into equations the Einsteinian propositions for the elaboration of a space-time continuum, an amalgamation of space and time in which, however, the latter preserves its independence (its direction is irreversible).

The nonmathematician, Einstein wrote, is apt to shudder at the mention of four dimensions. It is a feeling similar to that produced by the Phantom of the Opera. And yet there is nothing more banal than the statement that the world in which we live is a space-time continuum of four dimensions.

Space is a continuum of three dimensions. This means that it is possible to determine the position of a point (immobile) by means of three numbers (coordinates) x, y, z, and that for each point there exists a number of "neighboring points" whose position can be determined by the coordinates x', y', and z', which can be as near or as far as we wish from the coordinates of x, y, z of the first point. On account of this latter property, we speak of a continuum of three dimensions in consideration of the three coordinates.

In the same way the world of physical events, which Minkowsky simply called the "world," is naturally four-dimensional in this space-time sense. It is composed of individual events each of which is determined by four numbers—the three space coordinates x, y, and z and a time coordinate t.

The world in this sense is also a continuum because there exist for each event a certain number of "neighboring events" (realized or imagined) whose coordinates x', y', z', and t' differ at will from the coordinates x, y, z, t of the first event under consideration.

That we are not accustomed to consider the world as a four-dimensional continuum is explained by the fact that in pre-relativist physics time in relation to the space coordinates played a different and more independent role. In fact, according to classiçal mechanics, time is absolute—that is to say, independent of the position and the state of movement of the frame of reference. This is expressed in the final equation of the Galilean transformation ($t' = t$).

Thanks to the relativity theory the conception of a "world" of four dimensions becomes quite natural since, according to this theory, time is deprived of its total independence, as is shown by the fourth equation of the Lorentz transformation:

$$t' = \frac{t - \dfrac{v}{c^2} x}{\sqrt{1 - \dfrac{v^2}{c^2}}}$$

According to this equation the difference of time t' of two events in relation to K' does not usually cancel out, even if the difference of time t' cancels out in relation to K. The purely spatial difference of the two events in relation to K results in an interval of time of the same events in relation to K'.

This, however, does not constitute the importance of Minkowsky's discovery for the formal development of the relativity theory. It resides far more in the knowledge that the four-dimensional space-time continuum of the relativity theory represents in its basic properties the closest kinship with the three-dimensional continuum of Euclidian spatial geometry.

To emphasize this kinship to the full we must for the ordinary coordinate of time t substitute the imaginary length $\sqrt{-1}ct$ which is proportional to it. But then the laws of nature that satisfy the demands of the special theory of relativity take on mathematical forms where the coordinate of time plays exactly the same part as the three space coordinates. These four coordinates correspond exactly to the three space coordinates of Euclidian geometry.

THE EMPLOYMENT OF NON-EUCLIDIAN GEOMETRIES

The Euclidian postulates considered until the nineteenth century as the basis of all mathematical geometry and characterized by the famous axiom—*From a point outside a straight line one can only draw a single parallel to this straight line*— are nevertheless inventions of the human mind with no cosmic reality. The Euclidian definition according to which a straight line is the shortest distance between two points is valid only in the abstract, for human constructions and for extremely reduced spatial dimensions.

What does it mean in effect to maintain that we advance on earth "in a straight line," since we know that the earth is not flat but spherical. On the surface of this earth the shortest difference between two points, for example between New York and London, is not a straight line but a great circle embracing to the north Nova Scotia, Newfoundland, and Iceland. Thus, merely in the dimension of our planet Euclidian geometry reveals itself to be impracticable for portraying reality. If we wish to trace a huge triangle on a terrestrial globe from two points situated on the equator to the North Pole, the Euclidian theorem which maintains that *"the sum of the angles of a triangle is always equal to two right angles, in other words 180°"* will not be fulfilled. If in the same way we tried to trace a huge circle on the earth's surface (the point of a gigantic compass being placed on the equator following the River Congo, for example, while the tracing leg of the compass draws a circumference running south toward the Cape of Good Hope, to the north to the Nile Delta, to Liberia to the west and to somewhere near the Protectorate of Aden to the east) the relationship between the diameter (represented approximately by a pseudo-straight line drawn on a planisphere from Port Said to the Cape) and this circumference would be less than the classic value π.

Any reader who possesses a terrestrial globe (preferably illuminated) can swiftly verify this without going into the mathematical details. He will see that his circle traced on the globe, which visually is no different from the one he could draw on the flat surface of a sheet of paper and which from the point of view of the length of circumference would have absolutely identical dimensions, has a diameter measured on the globe slightly larger than the one on the flat surface.

Let us imagine that some explorers, completely ignorant of the earth's structure, set out in a strict straight line from some point on the equator. Let us ignore the crossing of mountains and oceans. The notion of a straight line would be given them by the *geodesic* on the earth's surface, the latter in fact appearing to correspond to a part of the geometrical straight line, taking into account only small distances, but being in reality the arc of a huge circle of our earth. In any case our explorers *who have continued to march in their straight line* (or have been convinced that they have done so) will eventually return to their point of departure after having traveled some 24,800 miles.

Lobatchevski, Bolyai, Gauss, and finally Riemann had already asked themselves seriously in the nineteenth century if it were not possible to reject Euclid's postulate according to which *"From a point outside a straight line one can only draw a single parallel to this straight line."* But we have just seen that the idea of a straight line, completely clarified if we omit the imaginary implicit in Euclidian geometry (i.e. if we merely envisage the true facts and not simply the theory), already leads us to refute what Euclid and his successors maintained: *that a finite straight line can be prolonged indefinitely in two directions.* We maintain in fact that this is incorrect because a "straight line" is an imaginary creation, and that in reality only geodesics exist. Even if the curve of this geodesic is only slightly accentuated, it is never nil, and just as our travelers following a pseudo-straight line and supposing that they never deviated from this pseudo-rectilinear course would find themselves back at their point of departure, the same would apply to a ray of light *if the latter did not propagate in a straight line.*

THE ATTACK ON THE INVARIANCE OF THE VELOCITY OF LIGHT

To demonstrate that light does not *necessarily* propagate in a straight line from the relativist point of view, Einstein resorted once more to the example of the elevator moving in space at a constant acceleration.

Let us substitute for this image a space rocket accelerated by a nuclear fuel in such a way that its acceleration corresponds to g—the symbol of the acceleration of the gravity of our globe, i.e. about 10 m/s. Now let a meteorite pierce the armor-plating of the cabin in such a way that it enters by one of the side walls in the direction of its progress and emerges from the opposite side. Without taking into account the physical effects of the shock and the slowing down that would occur (we are still in the domain of fiction and can ignore the effects of decompression) the passengers would find that the hole made by the meteorite as it left the cabin would be slightly below that on the other side. Why? Simply because while the meteorite crossed the cabin the latter continued its forward accelerated movement and the rectilinear course of the meteorite (and relative to the accelerated cabin) was deviated to the same extent.

This is the conclusion to which an outside observer would come. But if the travelers were convinced that they were not in a spaceship in constant acceleration, but in the earth's gravitational field (because of the acceleration of 10 m/s^2), they might deduce that the meteorite was a shell fired by a cannon from the earth and that this shell had quite normally described a parabolic curve under the influence of the earth's attraction.

In the meantime, the cabin continues its accelerated movement as if nothing had happened, but now a few moments later a ray of light traverses the hole made by the meteorite. Naturally, since the velocity of light is far greater than that of a meteorite or a shell propelled by the best explosive known (even by a nuclear explosive), the ray would not go out by the other hole, but would strike the wall above this hole. And yet the "point of impact" would be situated an infinitesimal fraction of a millimeter below the horizontal of the first hole.

The travelers who had totally forgotten that they were in a spaceship and who believed that they were still on the ground, having on the other hand forgotten the laws of general relativity, would be greatly perplexed.

They were convinced that light travels in a rectilinear manner—that is to say, solely in a straight line, but now, like any ordinary material object such as a shell or a meteorite, does it not suddenly possess a *curved trajectory?*

However, recalling the laws of special relativity, our physicists would have one course left: to admit according to the Einsteinian equation $m = \dfrac{E}{c^2}$ (m the mass is equal to E the energy divided by the velocity of light squared) that light, which is a form of energy and therefore similar to mass, can be influenced by a gravitational field, and thus, the ray of light has a curve analogous to the trajectory of a massive object (shell or meteorite).

Starting from this basis Einstein came to the logical conclusion that the light of the stars that, by an effect of perspective, are situated to our eyes close to the sun, could be curved in the neighborhood of the heavenly body, and that in consequence photographs of these stars should make them appear for observers on earth slightly shifted from their "normal" positions in the sky—that is to say, from the ones they occupied when seen from the earth—the effect of perspective making them appear distant from the sun (we must not forget that the sky appears to us as a sphere studded with fixed stars moving around us).

The difficulty was that the stars are invisible in broad daylight and naturally the sun disappears at night. There were only a few occasions when the stars and the sun could be observed together—during total solar eclipses. This phenomenon is caused by the passage of the moon between the earth and the sun on the plane of the ecliptic—a rare coincidence, for the moon circles the earth on a somewhat inclined ellipse in relation to the plane of the ecliptic. The silhouette of the lunar disc then totally covers the solar disc, and the resultant obscuration allows the stars to be seen by observers located at that part of the globe where the phenomenon is visible in totality.

The first eclipse after the publication of the general theory took place on May 29, 1919. It was visible in certain equatorial regions and the élite of the astronomical world traveled there to observe it. Everyone was anxious to know the results of the photographic experiment which was to reveal whether the displacement foreseen by Einstein would take place or not. The deviation predicted was 1.75″ of the arc of a circle.

To the great confusion of the detractors of the theory, the average of the observations recorded was 1.64″, a very acceptable figure if one takes into account the imprecision of the instruments.

It was not evident by the special theory alone that the variations of inert mass would be accompanied by variations of weight. But by demonstrating that gravitation acts on energy in the same way that it acts on masses, Einstein acquired the certitude. Furthermore, experiment showed that when light travels in a parabolic trajectory its velocity would no longer be invariable. (It remans unsurpassable, but in a field of gravitation it undergoes the relativist effect of the slowing down of the clocks known as the "Einsteinian effect.")

The "Einsteinian effect" is very different from the Doppler effect. The latter indicates that if a source of light emitting a radiation of a known wavelength recedes from the observer, the spectral ray corresponding to this radiation (modifications due to the composition of the velocity of the luminous waves with the speed of displacement from the source) will tend toward the red (if, on the contrary, the source approaches the observer, it will tend toward the violet).

With the "Einsteinian effect" that true clock, the atom, has to prove its slowing down by emitting light of a lower frequency than that of the atom of an identical element situated on earth: the spectral rays of an atom situated in a more intense field of gravitation (let us recall the experiment with the rotating disc) should deviate toward the red.

As regards an atom forming part of the solar atmosphere in relation to an atom whose vibrations were measured on the earth, the modification to be revealed to confirm the new Einsteinian postulate was very small (0.011 ångström), but despite the numerical difficulties of such a fine verification, the shift was found to be true. The slowing down of the clocks by the effect of gravity was also established thanks to the White Dwarfs, which are stars of unusual density (50,000 times that of water in the case of the companion of Sirius, for example). Here the displacements of the spectral rays were considerable, and fully confirmed this essential postulate of the general theory of relativity.

ON THE CURVE OF SPACE-TIME

The formulae of the special theory were conceived in such a way that the invariance of the electromagnetic laws were assured when the observer carried out observations with any animated system of reference of uniform movement in relation to himself, that is to say, of a constant speed in extent and direction.

But we have seen that this did not satisfy Einstein, who insisted that the physical laws should be expressed so that they remained valid for all possible systems of reference *moving in any absolute fashion whatsoever.*

The general relativity theory had to produce formulae of transformation from which it would be possible to define a metric, so that with the resultant gauges of space and time it would be possible for an observer situated at any point of the universe to study the phenomena which took place there, and with regard to the latter making use of all possible frames of reference and always in uniform or nonuniform movement in relation to himself.

By and large this meant abandoning the formula "in relation to . . ."

Such a result had to be obtained by a whole series of transformations, the details of which we have no space to discuss here. We must remember that as a result of his elaboration of the general relativity theory Einstein denied all physical reality to the force of gravity and turned in the main toward the movement of masses: *"If a determined body sees its trajectory deviated by a gravitational field,"* he postulated, *"we must not consider that it is a question of a material action* [in the sense of Newtonian gravity or of classical mechanics] *exercising itself on this body, but admit that in a field of gravitation the metric of space is modified* [the basic standards of time and length according to the various trajectories are altered] *so that the trajectory of a body left to itself will cease to be a straight line and will appear curved by reason of the alteration of this metric."*

Classical mechanics teach us that in space, in the absence of all external action, the trajectory of a body left to itself is a straight line traversed at a uniform movement, for the straight line represents the shortest distance between two points in space; but we have already seen that the notion of a straight line so far as a sphere is concerned is replaced by that of the geodesic (in ordinary three-dimensional space). One should therefore say that *"any body left on a plane surface which is not subjected to any action, displaces itself according to a geodesic of this plane surface."*

The general relativity theory transposes this postulate in the following manner: *"Any body left to itself in space and subjected to no action displaces itself according to a space geodesic."* Of that space, therefore, where the metric is altered by the fields of gravitation; in other words by the presence of matter—stars, planets, etc.

Let us take a planet: If a meteorite passes close to it (in its field of gravitation), it will be observed that the trajectory of the meteorite ceases to be rectilinear: if its speed is such that it compensates for the attraction of the planet very exactly by the effect known as "centrifugal force," the meteorite will become a permanent satellite of the latter. (If this speed is insufficient, the meteorite will fall onto the planet.) If on the other hand its speed is very great, it will pursue its path after having been deviated by the field of gravitation (the trajectory becomes a hyperbola).

Classical mechanics concluded from such observations, having their corollary in the gravitation of planets around the sun, of comets around the same sun, of satellites around the planet, and in particular of the moon around the earth, which with its speed of translation of .62 m/s compensates very exactly at its distance for the attraction of the earth, a *gravitational action* exercised by mass on mass. (But it must be noted that if the moon gravitates around the earth, the earth also gravitates around the moon and this axiom holds good for all universal phenomena.) Now Einstein says: *"There is no action between masses at a distance: the existence of masses* [or, to be more precise, the field of gravitation that these masses create] *has the effect of deforming space by locally changing its metric so that the geodesic of this disturbed space ceases to be a straight line."* Whence the statement: space is curved in the vicinity of masses, or more generally speaking because of the presence of all the bodies punctuating space: *space is a curve.*

This is certainly not a view of intuition. Newton's law of gravity accounts for the movement of the planets, *a priori,* for the latter are slow-moving compared with the velocity of light. It was, however, one planet of the solar system which, on account of its proximity to the sun on the one hand, and on account of its greater orbital speed on the other, failed to fulfill the exact conditions of the Newtonian laws, according to which a planet should describe a permanent ellipse (in relation to the so-called fixed stars and ignoring the gravitational influence of other planets). This was the planet Mercury.

Mercury is relatively very near the sun since it is only some 36 million miles average distance away from it. Now Leverrier had proved long ago that in relation to the so-called fixed stars this planet's orbit had a very slow rotation (43″ of an arc per century—in other words, one revolution in three million years) in the plane of the orbit and in the direction of the planet's movement of revolution (a precession also observed in the trajectory of electrons around the nucleus of the atom).

Leverrier had tried to explain the phenomenon by suggesting that there was a small invisible planet, which he named Vulcan, between the sun and Mercury, but Vulcan was never discovered, simply because it did not exist. The general relativity theory alone accounted for the phenomenon with sufficient accuracy so that it could be taken as proof of the validity of the Einsteinian postulates: considering in effect that Mercury describes a geodesic in the continuum whose metric is determined by the mass of the sun, one obtains as a representation of its orbit a nonclosed curve, i.e. that the pseudo-elliptic trajectory thus defined shows, in the orbital direction of movement, a slow rotation whose value gives an approximate advance of 42.85″ to 42.91″ of an arc per century.*

All the planets undergo similar modifications of their ellipses, but given that the effect is less and less appreciable proportionate to their distance from the sun (less gravita-

* Several recent observations carried out with the aid of radar and by the determination of the movement of space rockets (particularly by NASA) have revealed appreciable differences between the experimental and the theoretical results. It is not impossible that the laws of gravity, including the relativist corrections, may shortly be revised.

tional effect, less orbital speed) it has only been possible so far to make comparative verifications in the cases of Venus and the Earth. The latter irrefutably confirm that for the whole of the solar system, the planets describe "nonclosed curves" (and not ellipses), from which it can be maintained that according to the duration of geological time, the relative positions of the different planetary orbits have constantly been modified according to the laws of general relativity.

This verification can perhaps be a great aid to our understanding of all kinds of geological phenomena during the earth's past.

EINSTEIN'S UNIVERSE

It is no longer possible to doubt the validity of the representation of the non-Euclidian space-time continuum of general relativity by mathematics. It is, however, very difficult, if not impossible, to obtain a concrete image of such a universe, because of the introduction of time as the fourth coordinate, on the one hand, and on the other because of the idea of curvature which is not only spatial but also temporal: in the vicinity of masses it is not only the ray of light that bends, but also the time of photons that slows down; or to be more exact, it is the space-time interval that contracts, determining the said curve.

Jeans described Einstein's universe as a "soap bubble with a wrinkled surface." He went on to explain, "The universe is not inside the soap bubble but on the surface, and we must always remember that whereas the surface of the soap bubble has two dimensions, the universe has four—three space dimensions and one time dimension. And the substance through which the bubble has been blown, the soap foam, is only an empty void filled with empty time."

Such an analogy does not really hold water. The universe cannot be something with nothing inside it and nothing around it—this is tantamount to saying that it is of space and time (created by the presence of matter) in "the void."

Everything proves (or else the relativity of simultaneity would have no justification) that the universe has an area, length, breadth, and thickness: so much for the three space coordinates. Everything also proves the movements of bodies, relative to each other—whence the time coordinate. One is naturally inclined to imagine a kind of gas whose molecules are animated by *regulated* movements; these molecules (stars, planetary systems, stellar systems, galaxies, and galactic systems) interfering with each other in an incessant "mixing" that in any case deprives all ideas such as a "center" or a "periphery" of the universe of any significance.

Einstein writes: "We could represent our world as behaving, from the geometric point of view, like a surface irregularly curved in detail [on account of the presence of matter and the existence of gravitational fields], but which does not diverge in any appreciable manner from a plane, as for example the surface of a lake disturbed by small ripples. We could also call such a world quasi-Euclidian. But calculations show that in a quasi-Euclidian world the average density of matter would be zero. Such a world could not therefore be peopled everywhere with material. . . . But if in the world the average density of matter diverges, however little, from zero, then the world is no longer quasi-Euclidian. Calculations show on the contrary that if matter were uniformly distributed, the world would of necessity be spherical or elliptical. But since in actual fact matter is in detail irregularly distributed, the real world will in detail diverge from the spherical form—it will be quasi-spherical."

With this in mind, Einstein believed the universe to be "finite." "From the fact," he said, "that space is directly united to the matter it contains, this space could not be infinite since the presence of matter would have the effect of curving it locally."

The argument is contestable, and it is contested by the protagonists of an infinite universe, but in this book we are dealing with the ideas of Einstein and not with those of others even if we sometimes prefer the latters'. It is, however, necessary to remark that to say (not by Einstein, but by many of his critics): "The universe being spatially curved, light does not describe a geometric straight line, but a curved trajectory, implying that a ray of light will one day or another return to its point of departure," this is to forget the local distortions of relativist space that the said ray of light might encounter, and that would undoubtedly deviate it. In any case, even if the said ray of light propagated according to a perfect geodesic, it would not return to its point of departure (a star or any radiating body, and supposing it of course in an enclosed universe), but only to the "emplacement" of that point of departure (for the transmitting body would for its part have evolved on its own account).

If one admits the expansion of space, incontestable from the local point of view, for the totality of the universe, one must believe that the ray of light would never manage to "loop the loop," for since space dilates, it is obvious that the ray of light would always see its point of departure "fleeing in the distance. . . ."

At the start of his work Einstein considered a kind of static universe, but after the evidence produced by Hubble and Humason of the radial flight of the distant galaxies accessible to our observation, he envisaged a dynamic universe, broadly taking into account Georges Lemaître's hypothesis of the primeval atom.

According to this hypothesis, and as a result of numerous calculations concerning the average density of a finite universe, it has been calculated that our universe has a "probable radius" of six billion light years. Recent observations carried out with radiotelescopes indicate that radio sources appear to exist at distances exceeding 10 billion light years.

Admittedly this is no proof in favor of an infinite universe, and the Einsteinian image of a finite universe, unlimited in time and space (as the earth's surface would be unlimited for a being knowing only two dimensions, and in consequence no notion of the nature of a sphere), is still in favor among many astronomers.

It is probable that the true representation of the macrocosm still eludes us (as in fact does the microcosm), but to doubt the "Einsteinian Universe" does not detract from the solidity of both the special and general theories of relativity.

EINSTEIN'S THEORY OF THE UNIFIED FIELD

From 1920 until his death in 1955, Einstein worked obstinately on his elaboration of a theory of the unified field. Toward the end of his life he admitted that it was very improbable that this theory would be completed before his death to the complete satisfaction of physicists as far as the representation of the microcosm and macrocosm on identical mathematical bases was concerned.

Einstein's theory of the unified field tends radically to suppress the concept of action at a distance, i.e. to explain electromagnetic force as he explained the force of gravity in the general relativity theory, by deformations of the space-time metric.

The "force of gravity" having been postulated to be a fiction, he hoped to find equations that would allow him to conclude that electric charges curved space as did masses, so that other charges passing in their vicinity (in the electro-magnetic field) would obviously be deviated.

But the electric field is very different from the gravitational field. Whereas in space (i.e. without the braking action of the atmosphere) all bodies fall at the same speed, or rather assume the same acceleration irrespective of their mass, the same does not apply to electrified particles. The latter possess accelerations that vary according to the charges they bear. Furthermore, we must take into account the two inverse electric effects, the so-called "positive" and "negative" charges which should *a priori* confer opposite curves on space.

The most revolutionary aspect of Einstein's theory of the unified field was his proposal to reduce the theory of quanta to a simple consequence of the unified theory of fields itself. This hypothesis is rejected by most physicists. The notion of quantum action cannot in any way be separated from natural phenomena. It is indispensable.

It is indispensable in microphysics and it is quite possible that it extends to biological phenomena (evolution seems to have developed by quanta, and mutations also appear as quanta just as larval metamorphoses in their spontaneity are closely akin to quanta).

Although Einstein's relativity has been unanimously ac-cepted, this is far from the case with regard to his theory of the unified field. Numerous scientists, for example, have re-marked that this theory does not explain the behavior of the body in the vicinity of a single charge. Now the world of the atom is peopled by a host of these charges, and according to Heisenberg, in particular, he had to make up his mind to describe this world statistically (probabilities, the principle of uncertainties, etc.).

Nevertheless, many leading physicists are convinced that Einstein, on the whole, was on the right path. M. Louis de Broglie, to whom this book is dedicated and who until 1951 accepted the probability of interpretation, having modified his own wave mechanics to a certain extent, suddenly had the intuition, chiefly as a result of the works of Bohm and of his pupil Jean-Pierre Vigier, and also from the remarks of Schrö- dinger, that it was desirable, as he put it, "to return to precise space-time images, which allow one to understand clearly what one is talking about."

This illustrious academician, a Nobel Prize winner, con- cluded: "Today I consider it quite possible that the reinter- pretation of wave mechanics obtained by substituting for the waves normally considered continuous, 'true' waves hav- ing a singularity, may completely revolutionize quantum physics by allowing it mainly to describe the structure of various kinds of corpuscles and to forecast their properties; by allowing it thus to operate in conjunction with relativistic physics, conceived in the Einsteinian manner, as a general field theory."

De Broglie is working today in this direction.

For his part, Einstein wrote after recognizing that his hypotheses were not sufficiently supported by experiment: "The modern generation of physicists, in connection with the present-day form of the quantum theory, thinks that the state of a system cannot be characterized in a direct manner, but indirectly by indicating the statistics of the results obtained from the measures of the system. The predominant conviction is that duality (corpuscular and wave constructions), solidly proved by experiment, can only be entertained with an under- mining of reality. I am of the opinion that a theoretical renun- ciation which goes so far does not rest for the moment on our true knowledge, and that it must not prevent us from follow- ing the theory of the relativist field to the end."

Will the future prove him right? We do not know, but it is certain that a revolution is taking place in atomic physics, with regard to the proliferation of foreign particles, which could lead to a grandiose synthesis of the field theory, taking as its deep source Einstein's theory of the unified field.

5

Einstein the Fighter and the Persecuted

A DEEP-SEATED contradiction was to be found in Einstein: his complete detachment from everything concerning everyday humdrum life and his acute sense of duty toward the human race. He loved humanity as a whole but did not necessarily like individuals. An isolated misfortune often did not touch him, but he reacted to the sufferings of mankind.

Antonina Vallentin stresses this point: "He was spiritually free of all shackles, but at the same time morally involved. He was solitary, inaccessible, and at the same time passionately at one with his fellow men. He was very aware of this duality in his character. His monastic life, scarred with passionate interventions for causes dear to him, can really only be understood in the light of this duality. On the other hand he never ceased to stress the scientist's duty toward humanity."

"Solicitude for man and his future must always be the main interest of all technical efforts: never forget this in the midst of your diagrams and equations," he remarked one day.

"To Einstein," concludes Antonina Vallentin, "the scientist in his ivory tower was always a ridiculous and contemptible figure."

He often summed up his own efforts with this lapidary phrase: *"Only a life lived for others is worth living."* Disconcerted at the outset by his own fame, he accustomed himself to it as a powerful means of spreading ideas which he considered useful for human progress, and he seemed to consider himself more and more indebted to humanity as his fame increased.

It was because the Jews were persecuted that this man, completely detached from religious dogma and nationalism, became to a certain extent the "standard-bearer" of Zionism. He had renounced the Jewish faith. (We have already mentioned that he was educated by Catholics.) In fact he repudiated all the churches although he himself professed a kind of "cosmic religion"; but he could not tolerate that a group of men should be tormented on account of their beliefs.

"It was on my arrival in Germany," he explained, "that I discovered I was a Jew, and I owe this discovery more to non-Jews than to Jews."

At the time of his appointment to Berlin there already existed a latent anti-Semitism (sporadic and at times more or less accentuated, as in France and elsewhere in the so-called Christian world). The universities did not escape: very much the opposite—the phenomenon was more virulent there than elsewhere. For him perhaps the bitterest blow was to realize that in this atmosphere of hostility and even of contempt, certain Jews were ashamed of the hazard of their birth, becoming more anti-Semite than the most rabid anti-Semites, as though to do penance for some imagined blemish. In those days he wrote rather sadly: "I have seen the despicable mimicry of estimable Jews and my heart bled."

But he did not see the Jewish people, "my people" as he was often to call them, as a warlike and conquering nation, and if he finally became a militant Zionist, it was a reaction against Nazi persecution, the tortures and the death camps.

At the start of one of the most somber episodes in German history, before the paranoiac Hitler had come to power but when his arrogant minions had begun their racial persecutions, Einstein refused to share his friends' anxiety. Immersed in his study of the unified field, the rumors of what men call the "real world" reached his ears only in muffled tones. Heinrich Mann had tried to sum up the situation intelligently: "The reactions of a minority have no deep influence on a nation. Such experiences have no permanent character, they repeat themselves sporadically at some period or another, as one often finds the same words in the pages of a book. Do not let us be unduly disturbed. It will soon pass."

But progressively with the growth of National Socialism the

threats took shape. Soon not a week passed that the disappearance of some professor, writer, politician, or scientist was not reported, and an oppressive atmosphere of fear developed around Einstein. He himself was unafraid. Fear was a feeling alien to him. He said: "Hitler draws his strength from Germany's empty stomach, but as soon as the economic situation of the country improves this puppet will cease to play a role."

It was not long, however, before he was forced to see that the peril was very real. The suicide of Fritz Haber, a leading chemist and Nobel Prize winner, could have been caused by unjustified anxiety, but the murder of Walter Rathenau in broad daylight was a terrible warning.

Friends and admirers from all quarters begged him to flee from this Germany where, on account of his Jewish origin and despite his fame, he would not escape the insensate hatred of her new masters. He loved the peace of his little house at Caputh in the suburbs of Berlin, but above all he felt that he could still be useful to some of those who were being hunted. It needed the personal intervention of General von Seeckt for him finally to envisage his expatriation.

EINSTEIN VERSUS HITLER

Einstein had been approached by Princeton University with a view to teaching in the U.S. But although the American scientists held him in high esteem, the authorities were more reticent, and the stupidity of an official in the American Consulate in Berlin nearly ruined Einstein's plan of departure.

Marianoff tells the story very wittily: "Albert had received a letter asking him to come to the Chancellery in person to obtain his visa. He was rather surprised, for arrangements had already been made for him by a representative of the Hamburg-America Line. Nevertheless, he received the summons with good grace and went to the Consulate accompanied by Elsa."

This request for a personal interview was the result of a campaign in the American newspapers by a certain society of patriotic women who had lodged a protest with the State Department against his entering American territory on the pretext that he was a pacifist and nursed Communist aspirations.

"Albert," writes Marianoff, "had already been notified of this campaign. One evening he took his pen and retired to his study. A few minutes later, his eyes twinkling with mischief, he reappeared with a letter he had just composed and which he now read out to us with a laugh: 'I have never before been repulsed with such energy by the members of the fair sex at my first advances . . . or if it ever happened it was never by so many women at the same time. But are not these vigilant "citizenesses" perfectly right? Why open their gates to an individual who devours capitalists with the same appetite as the Minotaur in Crete devoured the ravishing Greek virgin and who, to make matters worse, was vile enough to reject any ideas of war, with the exception of the inevitable war with his own wife. In consequence do not ignore the advice of your wise patriotic women. Remember that Rome was once saved by the cackling of a few zealous geese.'

" 'Come, come, Albert, you really can't send that,' cried Elsa, horrified.

" 'And why not, pray?' asked Einstein, carefully sealing the envelope and stamping it."

But Einstein's wit had not been appreciated by the officials of the American Consulate in Berlin, and this is why he had been summoned. He "appeared" before a clerk, who casually turned over his file as he would have done for any undesirable immigrant.

"What is the purpose of your visit to the United States?" he asked coldly.

"The purpose?" repeated Einstein with stupefaction. "But to collaborate with your scientists."

"Is that so?" sneered the employee, with a superior air. "And what are your political opinions?"

"I have no political opinions," Einstein replied calmly.

"The employee," continued Marianoff, "proceeded with the interrogation with the air of a Torquemada during the Inquisition in Seville. Einstein began to realize that this was not a simple formality. He turned pale.

"Your compatriots have invited me to come to America," he burst out angrily, "This is the third invitation I have received, but if I am to be interrogated like a suspect, I won't go."

Musical relaxation with friends.
Behind Einstein, his wife

Einstein at the age of seventy-two

Einstein's vast circle of friends ranged from presidents and prime ministers to university undergraduates. Here he is shown (*above*) with Ben Gurion, and (*below*) with Pandit Nehru

Making his way over to the chair on which he had left his hat and coat, he left the Consulate, followed by the terrified Elsa.

Naturally the employee who had acted with such stupidity was discredited, for the press got wind of the affair and the State Department was deluged with indignant protests. Einstein finally received his passport at home without being disturbed and could leave for America.

The coming to power of Hitler and his clique took Einstein by surprise in his California retreat, just as he was preparing to return to Europe. What was to be done? To return to Germany would certainly entail persecution, because he was not the type of man to remain silent, and the Nazis were not the type of people to allow him to speak. He sailed, nevertheless, but the news he heard on the boat was far from encouraging: the "liquidation" was in full swing. But Elsa was anxious about her daughters and all their own possessions which were still in Germany. In these conditions how could he choose?

Einstein was completely indifferent to worldly goods. Reassuring Elsa, he decided against returning to his house in Caputh. His royal namesake, King Albert of the Belgians, offered him hospitality, and Queen Elizabeth, with whom he kept up a correspondence (they liked making music together), appended her cordial invitation to that of her husband. Letters and telegrams arrived from all over the world. Governments, colleagues, and private people offered him hospitality in palaces or in humble dwellings, but he chose the Belgian offer.

Immediately on his arrival in Europe, Einstein published the following declaration: "As long as the possibility remains open to me, I shall only live in a country where all its citizens enjoy political freedom, tolerance, and equality in the eyes of the law. Political freedom means freedom to be able to express in speech or in the written word one's political convictions; tolerance is the respect for the individual's convictions. Now today these conditions are not fulfilled in Germany. People who have especially deserved international understanding, including certain very eminent artists, have been persecuted. As in the case of every individual, every social organism can become psychologically ill, particularly at periods when life is hard. Nations usually recover from such maladies. I hope that Germany will soon be restored to health and that in future great men like Kant and Goethe

will not only be fêted from time to time, but that the principles they taught will be asserted in public life, and in the
general conscience."

This very moderate declaration aroused the fury of the
Nazis. A vast "smear" campaign was instituted against Einstein. He was asked to resign from the Prussian Academy of
Science. The latter reproached him for his "hostile attitude
toward the German people." But Einstein had only stigmatized its new masters: the Jew-baiters, Communists, Socialists,
pacifists, all an integral part of the German race. We must
never forget that the sinister camps at Dachau, Oranienburg,
and Buchenwald were opened for Germans!

Einstein was also a member of the Bavarian Academy. This
body also questioned him angrily on the attitude he had
adopted and asked him "how he envisaged his relationship
with the Academy in future." Einstein sent in his resignation.

On this occasion he wrote: "Academies first and foremost
have a mission to animate and protect the scientific life of a
country. Now as far as I know the German scientific societies
have allowed without protest a considerable number of German scholars and students, in addition to members of the
liberal professions with high academic qualifications, to be
deprived of their means of existence and of work in Germany.
I would never belong to a community which, even under external pressure, adopted such an attitude."

For many Germans, including the German Jews who hoped
that an exemplary passivity would save their skins and their
fortunes, Einstein became a traitor—the traitor.

"Anti-Semites are only too ready to speak of the malice and
cunning of the Jews," Einstein said later. "Has a more strik-
ing example of collective stupidity than the blindness of the
German Jews ever been seen before in history?"

Moreover, their coreligionists abroad did not always dis-
play a reaction of humanitarian solidarity. To quote Antonina
Vallentin: "In May, 1933, a relief committee for German
Jews was formed in Paris. This first wave of immigrants, consisting of penniless intellectuals, small tradesmen, and poor
Jews, preoccupied their French brothers. . . . I was invited to
a select meeting where the measures to be taken in view of
the increased wave of immigration were to be discussed. This
meeting took place at the house of a rich French industrialist.

'We are prepared to welcome the Jewish élite you mentioned,' said my host.

" 'It's not solely Jewish,' replied Antonina, 'there are also some far-sighted non-Jewish Germans who have left a country where intellectual freedom no longer exists. It is not a Jewish question to fight against Nazism, for the extermination of the Jews is only part of the National Socialist program.'

" 'But our chief concern is the Jews,' insisted the industrialist. 'Of what elements is the Jewish diaspora composed, and what can we do for them? We must above all avoid admitting those who could compete with the French. Immigration might provoke anti-Semitism here. . . .'

" 'The old current slogan!' cried Antonina Vallentin. 'I keep hearing: "National interest" . . . "noninterference in the internal politics of a country" . . . "France must not provoke Germany" . . . "Legitimate humanitarian feelings must not blind us to our real interests." ' The conscience of the world lay at our feet, on the Persian rugs of this luxurious drawing room."

"The haves combine together to defend themselves against the have-nots," was Einstein's comment.

Albert and Elsa settled down temporarily on Belgian soil near the little North Sea resort, Le Coq.

The French Minister of National Education, Anatole de Monzie, would have liked Einstein to teach at the Collège de France. Einstein had many other offers: from the Princeton Institute for Advanced Study and from Oxford, Leyden, Madrid, and Brussels, but he decided to give the preference to France. "I'll see about the others," he said.

In a public declaration thanking the French people for their hospitality, he wrote: "I know that the moral forces are still alive in France and that on the Continent of Europe they support the highest traditions—those traditions of spiritual and political freedom which are today so grievously threatened. The prospect of being able with my French friends to engage in an activity in the service of science fills me with joy."

One of these friends was Paul Langevin, whom Einstein often maintained could quite easily have discovered the laws of relativity. Then there was Marie Curie, whom he considered far superior to many male physicists, and finally Paul Painlevé.

But the conservative academicians would have had to transform the Chair of Teutonic Studies, which had become vacant as a result of Andler's death, into a Chair of Physics. In theory this was simple enough. However, the chauvinism of some and the intrigues of others who in their mediocrity did not like being eclipsed by the brilliance and knowledge of Einstein sabotaged this fine plan. De Monzie then asked the Finance Committee of the Chamber to create a Chair of Physics. The attempt came up against similar difficulties, and Einstein was finally ousted from the so-called country of liberty.

In the autumn of 1933, he sailed for America and in particular to take up his post at Princeton University. This was the future scene of his activities and from where he was to fight as a philosopher, a thinker, a scientist, and as a man, strengthened by his powerful genius. It was at this period that he wrote:

"In the lightning flashes of our stormy age we see men and things in all their nakedness. Nations and individuals reveal their plans, strengths, weaknesses, and passions. Routine is of no possible use in the rapidly changing conditions of life. The conventions fall like ripe ears of corn."

AGAINST THE WAR AND IN FAVOR OF THE ATOMIC BOMB

No pacifist ever expended more in the cause of peace than Albert Einstein, and yet it was undoubtedly he who in 1939, before the United States had entered the war—although everyone knew that this was a matter of time—suggested to Roosevelt that the odious nuclear bomb could be made. Without him, let us face it, the crime would still have been committed. Moreover, anyone who had "an uneasy conscience" knows that he has no right to accuse Einstein. Only someone who has never made a mistake has this right, and we know that such a being does not exist anywhere in the world and that he never will exist.

Einstein was never the father of the release of nuclear energy, as has so often been maintained. As early as 1906, after the discovery of natural radioactivity by Becquerel and the subsequent experiments carried out by Pierre and Marie

Curie, he showed that matter is no more than concentrated energy, and that in theory this energy can be released.

A whole galaxy of scientists worked on the fulfillment of this astonishing prophecy: Rutherford, Niels Bohr, Frédéric and Irène Joliot-Curie, Otto Hahn, Strassmann, Lise Meitner, and Enrico Fermi, to quote only a few of the illustrious names which spring to mind.

This does not mean to say that Einstein did not "press the button" to release the bomb. He did not deny this himself, but it was the sorrow of his old age that he had done it.* But there was the great fear—not for himself, but for the future of the human race—of Nazi domination. The Hitlerites would not have hesitated for a moment to make the bomb and to use it to the maximum had they possessed the material means of bringing about the essential chain reaction. Heisenberg had received precise orders on this subject. It is true that Heisenberg—no more than Frédéric Joliot-Curie in Paris —did not dispose of enough fissile material to obtain reactions on the industrial plane, prior to the realization of a plutonium bomb. Above all he "retarded" the plan as much as he could because he was far from appreciating Hitlerian methods. He could, however, have been replaced by one of the 200 specialists working under his direction, who were not necessarily anti-Nazi, that is to say as opposed to Heisenberg, and who would have continued their research to the maximum. It would also have been possible for Germany to perfect a "revolutionary" method of isotopic separation of the eminently fissile U-235,† eliminating the intermediary stage of construction of a plutonium reactor. In short Einstein feared that the Nazis would perfect a nuclear bomb before the Allies; this would naturally have completely changed the outcome of the war —in other words, have given them the victory with all the consequences it implied for the freedom of the world. Moreover, it was legitimate to suppose that the Americans would use the monstrous weapon in a less barbarous way than the Germans. It was in this context that he wrote to Roosevelt, at the express wish of other physicists, his colleagues.

* "Had I known that the Nazis would not succeed in making the bomb before the Allies," he repeated several times, "I should have abstained from any participation."

† Uranium 235, an isotope of uranium.

It was primarily a question of drawing the President's attention to the terrifying reality—the possibility of transforming matter into energy by a process of fission of an atom nucleus of an explosive nature. Joliot-Curie, von Halban, and Kowarski in Paris had established this possibility in theory. The plans were in the hands of the Americans, showing how this could be realized. Fermi had just perfected a satisfactory principle of chain reaction to produce plutonium from uranium metal. It was now only a question of finding the uranium. . . .

This demanded enormous investment beyond the scope of any industrial concern. Moreover, the "business" was too specialized to interest any particular financial group, however adventurous.

A chain reaction in a bomb (explosive fission) can only be realized with what is called "eminently fissile matter," such as the isotope 235 of uranium or plutonium.

At the time no one was very sure of the quantity of the material necessary to make a bomb, since the figures ranged between 10 and 100 kilos. In any case, no one possessed more than a few grams of Uranium 235 and practically no plutonium.

The isotope 235 of uranium pre-exists only in the proportion of 7 per 1,000 in a volume of uranium metal (the major part being U-238). The separation has to be effected by chemical (gaseous diffusion) or physical (electromagnetic selection) methods. Plutonium does not exist in the natural state and appears only as the result of transmutations that take place in the fission of nuclear reactors.

But in common with many other elements, uranium metal is not found in a pure state. It therefore has to be extracted from ores such as pitchblende. In very rich lodes it is found only in the proportion of 1 to 100 and in poor ores, which are still worth exploiting, in the proportion of 1 to 1,000.

Before the war no factory was equipped to produce an acceptable output. Uranium was only considered a worthless byproduct of the extraction of radium, which also originated from the same pitchblende.

On account of his fame, Einstein was chosen by his colleagues to encourage Roosevelt to persuade Congress to vote the enormous funds needed for what was known in code as the "Manhattan Project." At the outset these monetary allowances were small, but eventually no expense was spared, and not only was the extraction of pitchblende organized on a vast scale, notably in the Belgian Congo and later in Canada; not only were industrial stations built for the refinement of uranium metal, but, purely and simply extrapolating laboratory methods to speed up the project, there were built—(*a*) a factory for separating the isotope of Uranium 235 by the use of huge electromagnets (the electromagnetic process) and (*b*) a factory for the isotopic separation of this same uranium by gaseous diffusion.

But the most gigantic effort (due to Fermi and Szilard) was the building of the Hanford reactors on the model of the first Chicago "pile" and designed for the elaboration of plutonium. For the cooling system of these reactors America even went so far as to change the course of the Columbia River. . . .

A controversy now started as to whether Einstein simply signed the letter to Roosevelt or composed it himself. The question is no longer of importance, but it is almost certain that he merely appended his signature to a letter composed by Szilard. The tragedy was that no one listened either to Einstein, Szilard, or the vast majority of scientists who supported them, when after the Nazi capitulation they entreated that the bomb should not be used against the innocent inhabitants of Hiroshima and Nagasaki. The war had been won in any case and as has been clearly established today the monstrous hecatomb was not inevitable. *Einstein signed the second warning letter to Roosevelt,* accompanied by a very detailed memorandum from Szilard informing him of the monstrous consequences of a nuclear explosion but, according to Robert Jungk, "the two letters were still pending on the President's desk when he died suddenly on April 12, 1945."

Truman and his advisers ignored the warnings and pleas of the scientists and gave the military *carte blanche.* . . .

Before setting ourselves up as implacable judges we should have to search our own consciences. We should have to forget our cowardly relief at the cessation of the carnage. We should remember that we cried victory at the period without bothering about the price that this victory had cost the others. . . . We should also have to explain why we did not have the courage to make a gesture, however small, in recent times and

within the framework of our own country, to reprove and try
to repress certain other massacres and certain other barbarities
which, although they were not "nuclear," were no less in-
famous. . . .

6

The Last Years

DURING the last years of his life, when he was not perfecting his unified field theory, Einstein's whole time was devoted to the battle against injustice, on the one hand, and to his attempt to organize a world government capable of bringing total and final peace to the whole planet, on the other.

He tried to convince the Americans and the British to share the secret of the atom bomb with the Soviet Union, but his advice was ignored; it must be admitted that Soviet Russia did not in the least share his views on world organization. In this way his nonconformism alienated the former without being able to satisfy the latter.

He was accused of being a Communist "stooge," but he stigmatized many of the errors Stalin committed. Of Lenin he once said: "I respect him as a man who has sacrificed himself completely, and devoted all his energy to establishing social justice. I do not consider his methods practical, but one thing is certain: men of his caliber are the guardians and restorers of the human conscience."

I think it fair to say that he was both a *libertarian* and a *supporter of communities*. We reproduce here his point of view on the question of man as an integral part of society:

"Man is at the same time a lone individual and a social individual. As an individual he tries to safeguard his own existence and that of his dear ones, to satisfy his personal desires and to develop his innate faculties. As a social animal he tries to win the approval and affection of his fellows, to share in their pleasures, to console them in their griefs and to better their living conditions. It is the very existence alone of these often contradictory tendencies which explains the particular character of a man. Their specific combination determines to what extent an individual can establish his inner balance and contribute to the good of society. It is quite possible that fundamentally the relative force of these two tendencies is determined by heredity. But the personality which finally emerges is largely shaped by the milieu in which he happens to find himself during his development, by the structure of the society in which he grows up, by the tradition of that society and his appreciation of certain types of behavior.

"For the human individual the abstract concept 'society' means the sum total of his relations, direct and indirect, with his contemporaries and with past generations. He is capable of thinking, feeling, struggling, and working as an individual, but he depends so much on society—in his physical, intellectual, and emotional existence—that it is impossible to think of him or to understand him outside society. It is 'society' which provides man with food, clothes, housing, tools for his work, language, the form and the greater part of the content of his thought. His life is made possible by the labor and talents of millions of individuals of the past and the present, concealed in this little word 'society.'

"It is therefore obvious that the dependence of the individual on society is a natural fact which cannot be suppressed. . . ."

Einstein lucidly exposed the misdemeanors of a capitalist society: "We are faced," he wrote, "with an immense society of producers whose members constantly seek to deprive each other mutually of the fruits of their collective work—not by force, but in fact in conformity with legally established rules. In this connection it is important to take into account that the means of production—that is to say the whole productive capacity necessary to produce consumer goods and increased capital—can legally be, and are to a great extent, the private property of certain individuals."

After explaining that by "worker" he understood all those who have no share in the possession of the means of production, Einstein goes on: "To the extent that the working contract is 'free,' what the worker receives is determined not by the true value of the goods he produces but by the minimum of his needs and in relation to the number of workers who are in search of a job. It must be understood that, even in theory, the wages of the worker are not determined by the value of his product.

"Private capital tends to be concentrated in a few hands, partly because of the competition between capitalists and partly because technological development and the increasing division of labor encourage the formation of larger units of production at the expense of the smaller ones. The result of these developments is a capitalist oligarchy whose formidable power cannot effectively be curtailed, not even by a society which has a democratic political organization. This is true since the members of the legislative body are chosen by the political parties largely financed or otherwise influenced by private capital, which for all practical ends separates the electoral from the legislative body. The consequence being that the representatives of the people do not sufficiently protect the interests of the underprivileged. Moreover, in present-day conditions, the capitalists inevitably control directly or indirectly the chief sources of information (press, radio, education). It is thus extremely difficult and in most cases quite impossible for the citizen to arrive at objective conclusions and to make an intelligent use of his political rights.

"The situation ruling in an economy based on private capital is thus characterized by two important principles: firstly, the means of production (capital) are in private hands and the possessors dispose of them as they consider suitable; and secondly, the working contract is free. Admittedly a *purely* capitalist society in this sense does not exist. It must be noted, in particular, that the workers after long and bitter political struggles have managed to obtain for certain categories a better form of 'free working contract.' But taken as a whole the economy today does not differ very much from 'pure' capitalism.

"Production is with a view to profit and not for utility. There is no means of foreseeing that all those who are capable and desirous of working will always find employment. . . . Technological advances often result in an increase in unemployment rather than an alleviation of work with hardship for everyone. The spur of the profit motive in conjunction with the competition between the capitalists is responsible for the instability in the accumulation and utilization of capital, which leads to more and more serious economic slumps. Unlimited competition leads to a considerable wastage of work and to the mutilation of the individual's social conscience."

Einstein on the other hand expressly underlined the sinister role played by personal ambition, at the same time remarking that: "The absence of a stimulant of this nature would render human cooperation quite impossible." But is not this "other stimulant" *emulation,* of which ambition is merely a vulgar caricature?

In a speech given during the celebration of the Tricentenary of Higher Education in America, he said: "The desire to be approved by one's fellow men is certainly one of the most important forces which serve to bind this society together. In this complex of feelings, constructive and destructive forces are closely intermingled. The desire to be noticed and approved is a healthy motive (emulation), but the desire to be recognized as better, stronger, and more intelligent than one's fellow men can easily lead to an excessively egotistical psychological compromise, which could become prejudicial both to the individual and to the community. In consequence, teachers must refrain from using facile methods of encouraging individual ambition to make their pupils work more diligently. The Darwinian theory of the struggle for existence and its concomitant natural selection have been invoked by many people to authorize and encourage the competitive spirit. Certain people have even tried to prove, pseudo-scientifically, the need for a destructive contest between individuals in the domain of economic competition. But this is unjust, for man owes his strength in the struggle for existence to the fact that he is an animal living in a society. And just as in an ant heap a struggle between the individual ants is not essential for survival, in a human society a battle between individuals is not necessary for survival."

EINSTEIN AT THE END OF HIS LIFE

Einstein was invited on several occasions to visit the Soviet Union, but he never made up his mind to accept. He found certain constraints unbearable. Although he understood them as being temporarily necessary, he did not countenance them. He was fully aware of the immense problems the Soviets had to resolve. When a group of scientists attacked him courteously but firmly on the subject of certain of his ideas concerning world government, in which he believed, he replied: "Your taking refuge in isolationism is easy to understand when one realizes what your nation has suffered at the hands of foreigners over the past three decades: their intervention during the revolution, the German invasions with their plan to carry out mass liquidation of the civil population, and the systematic 'smear campaign' in the western press. But however comprehensible this desire for isolation may be, it still remains just as disastrous for yourselves as for all the other nations."

He loved America, and it was on account of this love that he deplored the excessive role played by the military in national and international politics. He denounced the pressures caused by exaggerated nationalism, giving rise to witch hunts and censorship of education, the press, and scientific research. "I must admit quite frankly," he wrote in 1947, "that the foreign policy of the United States since the end of the war has often reminded me irresistibly of the German attitude under the Emperor William II, and I know that I am not the only one to have observed and deplored this analogy."

Einstein, who had so much faith in mankind, sometimes despaired of man. He said sadly: "Adaptation to wartime objectives and activities has corrupted the mentality of man. The result being that intelligent, objective, and humane thought is almost without effect; it is suspected and persecuted as unpatriotic."

Einstein lost his wife Elsa in 1936. Mileva, his first wife, never left Switzerland. Of their two sons, the elder still practices his profession of engineer in the United States. Margot, one of Elsa's daughters, often came to live him at Princeton after her divorce from Marianoff, but he delighted in his solitude.

"I live," he said, "in that solitude which is so painful to the young but so delightful in maturity."

In actual fact he lived the life of a recluse at Princeton, a provincial city reminiscent of some old English medieval town. His house at No. 112 Mercer Street was on the fringe of of the town. In 1945 he resigned from teaching at the Institute for Advanced Study, but continued to work on research

for the university until his death. Many stories circulated about
him: the little girl who approached him with her arithmetical
problem; his habit of wandering about the street barefoot or in
sandals and an old pullover, sometimes eating ice cream.
These stories are true.

He aged suddenly, as men who have always been ageless
often do—adults from childhood whose perpetual thirst for
knowledge seems to give them eternal youth. This is how
Antonina Vallentin saw him in the evening of his life: "His
face is that of a tall old man, his shoulders are still firm, his
bare neck round and solid, but time has plowed deep furrows
in his full cheeks. The lines around his lips are very deep, and
his huge domed forehead is heavily lined. In the old days the
wrinkles formed when he was concentrating or when anger
made him frown, but when he laughed they disappeared just
as quickly. Today they are permanent, irregular and deep-set
beneath the powerful bridge of his nose. He is hollow at the
temples. A most touching change has taken place in his eyes:
the lids seem to have been seared by his gaze and the dark
brown extends in large mauve patches down his cheeks. The
brown and mauve contrast with his matte complexion and the
thin line of his bluish lips."

He had approached her with his heavy gait, and she was
overwhelmed and distressed to see him like this. But once
contact had been re-established, she found that he had not
become embittered, as she had feared, merely terribly tired.
His fine intelligence was unimpaired, nor had his enthusiasm
waned. "His eyes were hollow, but nothing had disturbed the
brilliance of his glance—that black inextinguishable fire. His
pale face seemed to be consumed internally, undermined by
his illness and his suffering. The hieroglyphs of pain had left
their mark on his flagging flesh, but his strength burst through
his eyes and triumphed over the rest of his declining body.
His huge head was extraordinarily powerful—as though purged
of all that remained of the man in the flesh. The head of a
visionary fettered to earthly contingencies. His presence
seemed more than ever to be on borrowed time. It was dis-
tressing and terrifying to sense this precarious and menaced
presence, but one felt it to be as true as ever, more poignantly
human, more bound to the world, and more intent upon
survival."

Alas, Albert Einstein was soon to die, far too soon. On April

18, 1955, at 7:15 A.M. he passed away in Princeton Hospital as a result of an inflammation of the biliary duct.

Remembering science beyond his death in his will, he bequeathed his brain and body to the Faculty of Medicine. His remains that were not used for the advancement of human knowledge were cremated fifteen hours later, without ceremony, as he had requested.

Paris, March 30th, 1961

CHOICE OF TEXTS

Das Bild von dem Gebäude ist nicht so ganz gut. Es
sind in Wahrheit drei Entwicklungsstadien (phasen).

Zuerst voraus: Allgemeine Indexsysteme sind
formale Bedingungen, welche die Wahl unter
den möglichen Theorien einschränken.
Die drei Etappen sind durch eine schrittweise
Verschärfung des ... allgemeinen Prinzips

1. Etappe Einschränkendes Prinzip: Die Gleichungen
der Physik sollen gelten für alle diejenigen Koordinatensysteme,
für welche die Vakuum - Lichtgeschwindigkeit
konstant ist

2. Etappe Allg. R. Theorie Einschränkendes Prinzip.
Die Gleichungen sollen gelten für alle Systeme,
die durch stetige Koordinatentransformationen
auseinander hervorgehen.
Diese Theorie bestimmt das Gesetz des
Gravitationsfeldes praktisch eindeutig, lässt
aber einen ziemlich weiten Spielraum für
die theoretische Darstellung des elektromagnetischen
Feldes etc

3. Etappe. Verallgemeinerte Gravitationstheorie (oder einheitliche Feldtheorie) Durch eine naheliegende Verallgemeinerung
des Gravitationsfeldes gelingt es, eine einheitliche feldtheoretische
Theorie des Gesamtfeldes aufzustellen.

Für diese Theorie spricht bisher nur ihre formale
Vollkommenheit. Infolge mathematischer Schwierigkeiten
in der Verwertung der erlangten Gleichungen ist es jedoch
einstweilen nicht möglich diese Theorie zu prüfen.
Während also 1. und 2. mit Sicherheit als zutreffend erkannt
sind, ist es bei 3 durchaus nicht der Fall.

(a)

A Few of Albert Einstein's Reflections

"For the most part I do the thing which my own nature drives me to do. It is embarrassing to earn so much respect and love for it. Arrows of hate have been shot at me too; but they never hit me, because somehow they belonged to another world, with which I have no connection whatsoever."
—*Out of My Later Years*, New York: The Philosophical Library, Inc., New York), p. 50.

"The cult of individuals is always, in my view, unjustified. To be sure, nature distributes her gifts unevenly among her children. But there are plenty of the well-endowed, thank God, and I am firmly convinced that most of them live quiet, unobtrusive lives. It strikes me as unfair, and even in bad taste, to select a few of them for boundless admiration, attributing superhuman powers of mind and character to them. This has been my fate, and the contrast between the popular estimate of my powers and achievements and the reality is simply grotesque. The awareness of this strange state of affairs would be unbearable but for one pleasing consolation: it is a welcome symptom in an age which is commonly denounced as materialistic, that it makes heroes of men whose goals lie

115

wholly in the intellectual and moral sphere. This proves that knowledge and justice are ranked above wealth and power by a large section of the human race."
—*Ideas and Opinions,* (New York: Crown Publishers, 1954),

p. 4.

"Concern for man himself must always constitute the chief objective of all technological effort, concern for the big, un-solved problems of how to organize human work and the distribution of commodities in such a manner as to assure that the results of our scientific thinking may be a blessing to mankind, and not a curse.

"Never forget this when you are pondering over your diagrams and equations!"
—*Einstein on Peace,* (New York: Simon and Schuster, 1960), p. 122.

"The American lives even more for his goals, for the future, than the European. Life for him is always becoming, never being."

— *Ideas and Opinions,* p. 5.

". . . the moral imperative is not a matter for church and religion alone, but the most precious traditional possession of all mankind. . . . For looked at from a simple human point of view, moral conduct does not mean merely a stern demand

to renounce some of the desired joys of life, but rather a
sociable interest in a happier lot for all men."
                    —*Out of My Later Years*, pp. 18-19.

"That a man can take pleasure in marching in fours to the
strains of a band is enough to make me despise him. He has
only been given his big brain by mistake; a backbone was all
he needed. This plague-spot of civilization ought to be
abolished with all possible speed. Heroism by order, senseless
violence and all the pestilent nonsense that goes by the name
of patriotism—how I hate them! War seems to me a mean,
contemptible thing: I would rather be hacked in pieces than
take part in such an abominable business. And yet so high, in
spite of everything, is my opinion of the human race that I
believe this bogey would have disappeared long ago, had the
sound sense of the nations not been systematically corrupted
by commercial and political interests acting through the
schools and the Press."
—*The World as I See It*, (New York: Covici-Friede, 1934),
                                                p. 241.

"My passionate sense of social justice and social responsibility has always contrasted oddly with my pronounced freedom from the need for direct contact with other human
beings and human communities. I went my own way and have
never belonged to my country, my home, my friends, or even
my immediate family, with my whole heart; despite the
existence of these ties, I have never lost an obstinate sense
of detachment, of the need for solitude—a feeling which increases with the years. One becomes sharply conscious, without too much regret, of the limits of mutual understanding
and sympathy between one's fellow creatures. One no doubt

loses something in the way of cheerful bonhomie; on the other hand, one is largely independent of the opinions, habits, and judgments of one's fellows and avoids the temptation to take one's stand on such insecure foundations."

—*The World as I See It,* p. 239.

"My pacifism is an instinctive feeling, a feeling that possesses me; the thought of murdering another human being is abhorrent to me. My attitude is not the result of an intellectual theory but is caused by a deep antipathy to every kind of cruelty and hatred. . . ."

—*Einstein on Peace,* p. 98.

"I am rarely enthusiastic about what the League of Nations has done or has not done, but I am always thankful that it exists."

—*The Fight Against War* (New York: John Day, 1933), p. 15.

"It is easier to win over people to pacifism than to socialism. Social and economic problems have become much more complex, and it is necessary that men and women first reach the point where they actually believe in the possibility of peaceful solutions. Once this has been accomplished, they may be expected to approach economic and political problems in a spirit of cooperation. I would say that we should work first for pacifism, and only later for socialism."

—*Einstein on Peace*, p. 124.

"I would unconditionally refuse all war service, direct or indirect, and would seek to persuade my friends to adopt the same position, regardless of how I might feel about the causes of any particular war."

—*Einstein on Peace*, p. 95.

"If, then, it is true that the axiomatic basis of theoretical physics cannot be extracted from experience but must be freely invented, can we ever hope to find the right way? Nay, more, has this right way an existence outside our illusions? . . .

"I answer without hesitation that there is, in my opinion, a right way, and that we are capable of finding it. Our experience hitherto justifies us in believing that nature is the realization of the simplest conceivable mathematical ideas. I am convinced that we can discover by means of purely mathematical constructions the concepts and the laws connecting them with each other, which furnish the key to the understanding of natural phenomena. Experience may suggest the appropriate mathematical concepts, but they most certainly cannot be deduced from it. . . . In a certain sense, therefore, I hold it true that pure thought can grasp reality, as the ancients dreamed."

—*Ideas and Opinions*, p. 274.

"It is true that convictions can best be supported with experience and clear thinking. On this point one must agree unreservedly with the extreme rationalist. The weak point of his conception is, however, this, that those convictions which are necessary and determinant for our conduct and judgments, cannot be found solely along this solid scientific way.

For the scientific method can teach us nothing else beyond how facts are related to, and conditioned by, each other. The aspiration toward such objective knowledge belongs to the highest to which man is capable, and you will certainly not suspect me of wishing to belittle the achievements and the heroic efforts of man in this sphere. Yet it is equally clear that knowledge of what *is* does not open the door directly to what *should be.* One can have the clearest and most complete knowledge of what *is,* and yet not be able to deduct from that what should be the *goal* of our human aspirations. . . . The knowledge of truth as such is wonderful, but it is so little capable of acting as a guide that it cannot prove even the justification and the value of the aspiration toward that very knowledge of truth.

—*Out of My Later Years,* pp. 21-22.

"Intelligence makes clear to us the interrelation of means and ends. But mere thinking cannot give us a sense of the ultimate and fundamental ends. To make clear these fundamental ends and valuations, and to set them fast in the emotional life of the individual, seems to me precisely the most important function which religion has to perform in the social life of man."

But Einstein has clearly defined what he understood by religion: "The highest principles for our aspirations and judgments are given to us in the Jewish-Christian religious tradition. It is a very high goal. . . . If one were to take that goal out of its religious form and look merely at its purely human side, one might state it perhaps thus: free and responsible development of the individual, so that he may place his powers freely and gladly in the service of all mankind. . . . If one looks at the substance rather than at the form, then one can take these words as expressing also the fundamental democratic position. The true democrat can worship his nation as little as can the man who is religious, in our sense of the term."

—Out of My Later Years, pp. 22, 23.

(b)

Einstein's Ethics and Outlook

WE ALL KNOW, from what we experience with and within ourselves, that our conscious acts spring from our desires and our fears. Intuition tells us that that is true also of our fellows and of the higher animals. We all try to escape pain and death, while we seek what is pleasant. We all are ruled in what we do by impulses; and these impulses are so organized that our actions in general serve for our self-preservation and that of the race. Hunger, love, pain, fear are some of those inner forces which rule the individual's instinct for self-preservation. At the same time, as social beings, we are moved in the relations with our fellow beings by such feelings as sympathy, pride, hate, need for power, pity, and so on. All these primary impulses, not easily described in words, are the springs of man's actions. All such action would cease if those powerful elemental forces were to cease stirring within us.

Though our conduct seems so very different from that of the higher animals, the primary instincts are much alike in them and in us. The most evident difference springs from the important part which is played in man by a relatively strong power of imagination and by the capacity to think, aided as it is by language and other symbolical devices. Thought is the organizing factor in man, intersected between the casual primary instincts and the resulting actions. In that way imagi-

"Morals and Emotions," *Out of My Later Years* (New York: Philosophical Library, 1950), pp. 15-28.

123

nation and intelligence enter into our existence in the part of servants of the primary instincts. But their intervention makes our acts to serve ever less merely the immediate claims of our instincts. Through them the primary instinct attaches itself to ends which become ever more distant. The instincts bring thought into action, and thought provokes intermediary actions inspired by emotions which are likewise related to the ultimate end. Through repeated performance, this process brings it about that ideas and beliefs acquire and retain a strong effective power even after the ends which gave them that power are long forgotten. In abnormal cases of such intensive borrowed emotions, which cling to objects emptied of their erstwhile effective meaning, we speak of fetishism.

Yet the process which I have indicated plays a very important part also in ordinary life. Indeed there is no doubt that to this process—which one may describe as a spiritualizing of the emotions and of thought—that to it man owes the most subtle and refined pleasures of which he is capable: the pleasure in the beauty of artistic creation and of logical trains of thought.

As far as I can see, there is one consideration which stands at the threshold of all moral teaching. If men as individuals surrender to the call of their elementary instincts, avoiding pain and seeking satisfaction only for their own selves, the result for them all taken together must be a state of insecurity, of fear, and of promiscuous misery. If, besides that, they use their intelligence from an individualist, i.e., a selfish standpoint, building up their life on the illusion of a happy unattached existence, things will be hardly better. In comparison with the other elementary instincts and impulses, the emotions of love, of pity and of friendship are too weak and too cramped to lead to a tolerable state of human society.

The solution of this problem, when freely considered, is simple enough, and it seems also to echo from the teachings of the wise men of the past always in the same strain: All men should let their conduct be guided by the same principles; and those principles should be such, that by following them there should accrue to all as great a measure as possible of security and satisfaction, and as small a measure as possible of suffering.

Of course, this general requirement is much too vague that we should be able to draw from it with confidence specific rules to guide the individuals in their actions. And indeed, these specific rules will have to change in keeping with changing circumstances. If this were the main difficulty that stands in the way of that keen conception, the millenary fate of man would have been incomparably happier than it actually was, or still is. Man would not have killed man, tortured each other, exploited each other by force and by guile.

The real difficulty, the difficulty which has baffled the sages of all times, is rather this: how can we make our teaching so potent in the emotional life of man, that its influence should withstand the pressure of the elemental psychic forces in the individual? We do not know, of course, if the sages of the past have really asked themselves this question, consciously and in this form; but we do know how they have tried to solve the problem.

Long before men were ripe, namely, to be faced with such a universal moral attitude, fear of the dangers of life had led them to attribute to various imaginary personal beings, not physically tangible, power to release those natural forces which men feared or perhaps welcomed. And they believed that those beings, which everywhere dominated their imagination, were psychically made in their own image, but were endowed with superhuman powers. These were the primitive precursors of the idea of God. Sprung in the first place from the fears which filled man's daily life, the belief in the existence of such beings, and in their extraordinary powers, has had so strong an influence on men and their conduct, that it is difficult for us to imagine. Hence it is not surprising that those who set out to establish the moral idea, as embracing all men equally, did so by linking it closely with religion. And the fact that those moral claims were the same for all men, may have had much to do with the development of mankind's religious culture from polytheism to monotheism.

The universal moral idea thus owed its original psychological potency to that link with religion. Yet in another sense that close association was fatal for the moral idea. Monotheistic religion acquired different forms with various peoples and groups. Although those differences were by no means fundamental, yet they soon were felt more strongly than the essentials that were common. And in that way religion often caused enmity and conflict, instead of binding mankind together with the universal moral idea.

Then came the growth of the natural sciences, with their great influence on thought and practical life, weakening still more in modern times the religious sentiment of the peoples. The causal and objective mode of thinking—though not necessarily in contradiction with the religious sphere—leaves in most people little room for a deepening religious sense. And because of the traditional close link between religion and morals, that has brought with it, in the last hundred years or so, a serious weakening of moral thought and sentiment. That, to my mind, is a main cause for the barbarization of political ways in our time. Taken together with the terrifying efficiency of the new technical means, the barbarization already forms a fearful threat for the civilized world.

Needless to say, one is glad that religion strives to work for the realization of the moral principle. Yet the moral imperative is not a matter for church and religion alone, but the most precious traditional possession of all mankind. Consider from this standpoint the position of the Press, or of the schools with their competitive method! Everything is dominated by the cult of efficiency and of success and not by the value of things and men in relation to the moral ends of human society. To that must be added the moral deterioration resulting from a ruthless economic struggle. The deliberate nurturing of the moral sense also outside the religious sphere, however, should help also in this, to lead men to look upon social problems as so many opportunities for joyous service towards a better life. For looked at from a simple human point of view, moral conduct does not mean merely a stern demand to renounce some of the desired joys of life, but rather a sociable interest in a happier lot for all men.

This conception implies one requirement above all—that every individual should have the opportunity to develop the gifts which may be latent in him. Alone in that way can the individual obtain the satisfaction to which he is justly entitled; and alone in that way can the community achieve its richest flowering. For everything that is really great and inspiring is created by the individual who can labour in freedom. Restriction is justified only in so far as it may be needed for the security of existence.

There is one other thing which follows from that conception—that we must not only tolerate differences between individuals and between groups, but we should indeed welcome them and look upon them as an enriching of our existence. That is the essence of all true tolerance; without tolerance in this widest sense there can be no question of true morality.

Morality in the sense here briefly indicated is not a fixed and stark system. It is rather a standpoint from which all questions which arise in life could and should be judged. It is a task never finished, something always present to guide our judgment and to inspire our conduct. Can you imagine that any man truly filled with this ideal could be content:—

Were he to receive from his fellow men a much greater return in goods and services than most other men ever receive?

Were his country, because it feels itself for the time being militarily secure, to stand aloof from the aspiration to create a supra-national system of security and justice?

Could he look on passively, or perhaps even with indifference, when elsewhere in the world innocent people are being brutally persecuted, deprived of their rights or even massacred?

To ask these questions is to answer them!

A. Einstein.

As the privileged knew him: in his library

Towards the end of his life

(c)

Physics and Reality

§ 1. GENERAL CONSIDERATION CONCERNING THE METHOD OF SCIENCE

IT HAS OFTEN BEEN SAID, and certainly not without justification, that the man of science is a poor philosopher. Why then should it not be the right thing for the physicist to let the philosopher do the philosophizing? Such might indeed be the right thing at a time when the physicist believes he has at his disposal a rigid system of fundamental concepts and fundamental laws which are so well established that waves of doubt can not reach them; but, it can not be right at a time when the very foundations of physics itself have become problematic as they are now. At a time like the present, when experience forces us to seek a newer and more solid foundation, the physicist cannot simply surrender to the philosopher the critical contemplation of the theoretical foundations; for, he himself knows best, and feels more surely where the shoe pinches. In looking for a new foundation, he must try to make clear in his own mind just how far the concepts which he uses are justified, and are necessities.

The whole of science is nothing more than a refinement of everyday thinking. It is for this reason that the critical thinking of the physicist cannot possibly be restricted to the examination of the concepts of his own specific field. He cannot proceed without considering critically a much more difficult problem, the problem of analyzing the nature of everyday thinking.

Out of My Later Years, pp. 59-85.

On the stage of our subconscious mind appear in colorful succession sense experiences, memory pictures of them, representations and feelings. In contrast to psychology, physics treats directly only of sense experiences and of the "understanding" of their connection. But even the concept of the "real external world" of everyday thinking rests exclusively on sense impressions.

Now we must first remark that the differentiation between sense impressions and representations is not possible; or, at least it is not possible with absolute certainty. With the discussion of this problem, which affects also the notion of reality, we will not concern ourselves but we shall take the existence of sense experiences as given, that is to say as psychic experiences of special kind.

I believe that the first step in the setting of a "real external world" is the formation of the concept of bodily objects and of bodily objects of various kinds. Out of the multitude of our sense experiences we take, mentally and arbitrarily, certain repeatedly occurring complexes of sense impression (partly in conjunction with sense impressions which are interpreted as signs for sense experiences of others), and we attribute to them a meaning—the meaning of the bodily object. Considered logically this concept is not identical with the totality of sense impressions referred to; but it is an arbitrary creation of the human (or animal) mind. On the other hand, the concept owes its meaning and its justification exclusively to the totality of the sense impressions which we associate with it.

The second step is to be found in the fact that, in our thinking (which determines our expectation), we attribute to this concept of the bodily object a significance, which is to a high degree independent of the sense impression which originally gives rise to it. This is what we mean when we attribute to the bodily object "a real existence." The justification of such a setting rests exclusively on the fact that, by means of such concepts and mental relations between them, we are able to orient ourselves in the labyrinth of sense impressions. These notions and relations, although free statements of our thoughts, appear to us as stronger and more unalterable than the individual sense experience itself, the character of which as anything other than the result of an illusion or hallucination is never completely guaranteed. On the other hand, these concepts and relations, and indeed the setting of real objects and, generally speaking, the existence of "the real world," have justification only in so far as they are connected with sense impressions between which they form a mental connection.

The very fact that the totality of our sense experiences is such that by means of thinking (operations with concepts, and the creation and use of definite functional relations between them, and the coordination of sense experiences to these concepts) it can be put in order, this fact is one which leaves us in awe, but which we shall never understand. One may say "the eternal mystery of the world is its comprehensibility." It is one of the great realizations of Immanuel Kant that the setting up of a real external world would be senseless without this comprehensibility.

In speaking here concerning "comprehensibility," the expression is used in its most modest sense. It implies: the production of some sort of order among sense impressions, this order being produced by the creation of general concepts, relations between these concepts, and by relations between the concepts and sense experience, these relations being determined in any possible manner. It is in this sense that the world of our sense experiences is comprehensible. The fact that it is comprehensible is a miracle.

In my opinion, nothing can be said concerning the manner in which the concepts are to be made and connected, and how we are to coordinate them to the experiences. In guiding us in the creation of such an order of sense experiences, success in the result is alone the determining factor. All that is necessary is *the statement* of a set of rules, since without such rules the acquisition of knowledge in the desired sense would be impossible. One may compare these rules with the rules of a game in which, while the rules themselves are arbitrary, it is their rigidity alone which makes the game possible. However, the fixation will never be final. It will have validity only for a special field of application (i.e. there are no final categories in the sense of Kant).

The connection of the elementary concepts of everyday thinking with complexes of sense experiences can only be comprehended intuitively and it is unadaptable to scientifically logical fixation. The totality of these connections—none of which is expressible in notional terms—is the only thing which differentiates the great building which is science from a logical but empty scheme of concepts. By means of these connections, the purely notional theorems of science become statements about complexes of sense experiences.

We shall call "primary concepts" such concepts as are directly and intuitively connected with typical complexes of sense experiences. All other notions are—from the physical point of view—possessed of meaning, only in so far as they are connected, by theorems, with the primary notions. These theorems are partially definitions of the concepts (and of the statements derived logically from them) and partially theorems not derivable from the definitions, which express at least indirect relations between the "primary concepts," and in this way between sense experiences. Theorems of the latter kind are "statements about reality" or laws of nature, i.e. theorems which have to show their usefulness when applied to sense experiences comprehended by primary concepts. The question as to which of the theorems shall be considered as definitions and which as natural laws will depend largely upon the chosen representation. It really becomes absolutely necessary to make this differentiation only when one examines the degree to which the whole system of concepts considered is not empty from the physical point of view.

Stratification of the Scientific System

The aim of science is, on the one hand, a comprehension, as *complete* as possible, of the connection between the sense experiences in their totality, and, on the other hand, the accomplishment of this aim *by the use of a minimum of primary concepts and relations*. (Seeking, as far as possible, logical unity in the world picture, i.e. paucity in logical elements.)

Science concerns the totality of the primary concepts, i.e. concepts directly connected with sense experiences, and theorems connecting them. In its first stage of development, science does not contain anything else. Our everyday thinking is satisfied on the whole with this level. Such a state of affairs cannot, however, satisfy a spirit which is really scientifically minded; because the totality of concepts and relations obtained in this manner is utterly lacking in logical unity. In order to supplement this deficiency, one invents a system poorer in concepts and relations, a system retaining the primary concepts and relations of the "first layer" as logically derived concepts and relations. This new "secondary system" pays for its higher logical unity by having, as its own elementary concepts (concepts of the second layer), only those which are no longer directly connected with complexes of sense experiences. Further striving for logical unity brings us to a tertiary system, still poorer in concepts and relations, for the deduction of the concepts and relations of the secondary (and so indirectly of the primary) layer. Thus the story goes on until we have arrived at a system of the greatest conceivable unity, and of the greatest poverty of concepts of the logical foundations, which are still compatible with the observation made by our senses. We do not know whether or not this ambition will ever result in a definite system. If one is asked for his opinion, he is inclined to answer no. While wrestling with the problems, however, one will never give up the hope that this greatest of all aims can really be attained to a very high degree.

An adherent to the theory of abstraction or induction might call our layers "degrees of abstraction"; but, I do not consider it justifiable to veil the logical independence of the concept from the sense experiences. The relation is not analogous to that of soup to beef but rather of wardrobe number to overcoat.

The layers are furthermore not clearly separated. It is not even absolutely clear which concepts belong to the primary layer. As a matter of fact, we are dealing with freely formed concepts, which, with a certainty sufficient for practical use, are intuitively connected with complexes of sense experiences in such a manner that, in any given case of experience, there is no uncertainty as to the applicability or non-applicability of the statement. The essential thing is the aim to represent the multitude of concepts and theorems, close to experience, as theorems, logically deduced and belonging to a basis, as narrow as possible, of fundamental concepts and fundamental relations which themselves can be chosen freely (axioms). The liberty of choice, however, is of a special kind; it is not in any way similar to the liberty of a writer of fiction. Rather, it is similar to that of a man engaged in solving a well designed word puzzle. He may, it is true, propose any word as the solution; but, there is only *one* word which really solves the puzzle in all its forms. It is an outcome of faith that nature —as she is perceptible to our five senses—takes the character of such a well formulated puzzle. The successes reaped up to now by science do, it is true, give a certain encouragement for this faith.

The multitude of layers discussed above corresponds to the several stages of progress which have resulted from the struggle for unity in the course of development. As regards the final aim, intermediary layers are only of temporary nature. They must eventually disappear as irrelevant. We have to deal, however, with the science of today, in which these strata represent problematic partial successes which support one another but which also threaten one another, because today's systems of concepts contain deep seated incongruities which we shall meet later on.

It will be the aim of the following lines to demonstrate what paths the constructive human mind has entered, in order to arrive at a basis of physics which is logically as uniform as possible.

§ 2. MECHANICS AND THE ATTEMPTS TO BASE ALL PHYSICS UPON IT

An important property of our sense experiences, and, more generally, of all of our experience, is its time-like order. This kind of order leads to the mental conception of a subjective time, an ordinating scheme for our experience. The subjective time leads then through the concept of the bodily object and of space, to the concept of objective time, as we shall see later on.

Ahead of the notion of objective time there is, however, the concept of space; and, ahead of the latter we find the concept of the bodily object. The latter is directly connected with complexes of sense experiences. It has been pointed out that one property which is characteristic of the notion "bodily object" is the property which provides that we coordinate to it an existence, independent of (subjective) time, and independent of the fact that it is perceived by our senses. We do this in spite of the fact that we perceive temporal alterations in it. Poincaré has justly emphasized the fact that we distinguish two kinds of alterations of the bodily object, "changes of state" and "changes of position." The latter, he remarked, are alterations which we can reverse by arbitrary motions of our bodies.

That there are bodily objects to which we have to ascribe, within a certain sphere of perception, no alteration of state, but only alterations of position, is a fact of fundamental importance for the formation of the concept of space (in a certain degree even for the justification of the notion of the bodily object itself). Let us call such an object "practically rigid."

If, as the object of our perception, we consider simultaneously (i.e. as a single unit) two practically rigid bodies, then there exist for this ensemble such alterations as can *not* possibly be considered as changes of position of the whole, notwithstanding the fact that this is the case for each one of the two constituents. This leads to the notion of "change of relative position" of the two objects; and, in this way, also to the notion of "relative position" of the two objects. It is found moreover that among the relative positions, there is one of a specific kind which we designate as "Contact."[1] Permanent contact of two bodies in three or more "points" means that they are united as a quasi rigid compound body. It is permissible to say that the second body forms then a (quasi rigid) continuation on the first body and may, in its turn, be continued quasi rigidly. The possibility of the quasi rigid continuation of a body is unlimited. The real essence of the conceivable quasi rigid continuation of a body B_0 is the infinite "space" determined by it.

In my opinion, the fact that every bodily object situated in any arbitrary manner can be put into contact with the quasi rigid continuation of a predetermined and chosen body B_0 (body of relation), this fact is the empirical basis of our conception of space. In pre-scientific thinking, the solid earth's crust plays the role of B_0 and its continuation. The very name geometry indicates that the concept of space is psychologically connected with the earth as an assigned body.

---

[1] It is in the nature of things that we are able to talk about these objects only by means of concepts of our own creation, concepts which themselves are not subject to definition. It is essential, however, that we make use only of such concepts concerning whose coordination to our experience we feel no doubt.

The bold notion of "space" which preceded all scientific geometry transformed our mental concept of the relations of positions of bodily objects into the notion of the position of these bodily objects in "space." This, of itself, represents a great formal simplification. Through this concept of space one reaches, moreover, an attitude in which any description of position is admittedly a description of contact; the statement that a point of a bodily object is located at a point P of space means that the object touches the point P of the standard body of reference B_0 (supposed appropriately continued) at the point considered.

In the geometry of the Greeks, space plays only a qualitative role, since the position of bodies in relation to space is considered as given, it is true, but is not described by means of numbers. Descartes was the first to introduce this method. In his language, the whole content of Euclidian geometry can axiomatically be founded upon the following statements: (1) Two specified points of a rigid body determine a distance. (2) We may coordinate triplets of numbers X_1, X_2, X_3, to points of space in such a manner that for every distance $P' - P''$ under consideration, the coordinates of whose end points are X_1', X_2', X_3'; X_1'', X_2'', X_3'', the expression

$$S^2 = (X_1'' - X_1')^2 + (X_2'' - X_2')^2 + (X_3'' - X_3')^2$$

is independent of the position of the body, and of the positions of any and all other bodies.

The (positive) number S means the length of the stretch, or the distance between the two points P' and P'' of space (which are coincident with the points P' and P'' of the stretch).

The formulation is chosen, intentionally, in such a way that it expresses clearly, not only the logical and axiomatic, but also the empirical content of Euclidian geometry. The purely logical (axiomatic) representation of Euclidian geometry has, it is true, the advantage of greater simplicity and clarity. It pays for this, however, by renouncing representation of the connection between the notional construction and the sense experience upon which connection, alone, the significance of geometry for physics rests. The fatal error that the necessity of thinking, preceding all experience, was at the basis of Euclidian geometry and the concept of space belonging to it, this fatal error arose from the fact that the empirical basis, on which the axiomatic construction of Euclidian geometry rests, had fallen into oblivion.

In so far as one can speak of the existence of rigid bodies in nature, Euclidian geometry is a physical science, the usefulness of which must be shown by application to sense experiences. It relates to the totality of laws which must hold for the relative positions of rigid bodies independently of time. As one may see, the physical notion of space also, as originally used in physics, is tied to the existence of rigid bodies.

From the physicist's point of view, the central importance of Euclidian geometry rests in the fact that its laws are independent of the specific nature of the bodies whose relative positions it discusses. Its formal simplicity is characterized by the properties of homogeneity and isotropy (and the existence of similar entities).

The concept of space is, it is true, useful, but not indispensable for geometry proper, i.e. for the formulation of rules about the relative positions of rigid bodies. In opposition to this, the concept of objective time, without which the formulation of the fundamentals of classical mechanics is impossible, is linked with the concept of the spacial continuum.

The introduction of objective time involves two statements which are independent of each other.

(1) The introduction of the objective local time by connecting the temporal sequence of experiences with the indications of a "clock," i.e. of a closed system with periodical occurrence.

(2) The introduction of the notion of objective time for the happenings in the whole space, by which notion alone the idea of local time is enlarged to the idea of time in physics.

Note concerning (1). As I see it, it does not mean a "petitio principii" if one puts the concept of periodical occurrence ahead of the concept of time, while one is concerned with the clarification of the origin and of the empirical content of the concept of time. Such a conception corresponds exactly to the precedence of the concept of the rigid (or quasi rigid) body in the interpretation of the concept of space.

Further discussion of (2). The illusion which prevailed prior to the enunciation of the theory of relativity—that, from the point of view of experience the meaning of simultaneity in relation to happenings distant in space and consequently that the meaning of time in physics is a priori clear—this illusion had its origin in the fact that in our everyday experience, we can neglect the time of propagation of light. We are accustomed on this account to fail to differentiate between "simultaneously seen" and "simultaneously happening"; and, as a result the difference between time and local time fades away.

The lack of definiteness which, from the point of view of empirical importance, adheres to the notion of time in classical mechanics was veiled by the axiomatic representation of space and time as things given independently of our senses. Such a use of notions—independent of the empirical basis, to which they owe their existence—does not necessarily damage science. One may however easily be led into the error of believing that these notions, whose origin is forgotten, are necessary and unalterable accompaniments to our thinking, and this error may constitute a serious danger to the progress of science.

It was fortunate for the development of mechanics and hence also for the development of physics in general, that the lack of definiteness in the concept of objective time remained obscured from the earlier philosophers as regards its empirical interpretation. Full of confidence in the real meaning of the space-time construction they developed the foundations of mechanics which we shall characterize, schematically, as follows:

(a) Concept of a material point: a bodily object which—as regards its position and motion—can be described with sufficient exactness as a point with coordinates X_1, X_2, X_3. Description of its motion (in relation to the "space" B_0) by giving X_1, X_2, X_3, as functions of the time.

(b) Law of inertia: the disappearance of the components of acceleration for the material point which is sufficiently far away from all other points.

(c) Law of motion (for the material point): Force = mass $\times$ acceleration.

(d) Laws of force (actions and reactions between material points).

In this (b) is nothing more than an important special case of (c). A real theory exists only when the laws of force are given. The forces must in the first place only obey the law of equality of action and reaction in order that a system of points

—permanently connected to each other—may behave like *one* material point.

These fundamental laws, together with Newton's law for gravitational force, form the basis of the mechanics of celestial bodies. In this mechanics of Newton, and in contrast to the above conceptions of space derived from rigid bodies, the space B_0 enters in a form which contains a new idea; it is not for every B_0 that validity is required (for a given law of force) by (*b*) and (*c*), but only for a B_0 in the appropriate condition of motion (inertial system). On account of this fact, the coordinate space acquired an independent physical property which is not contained in the purely geometrical notion of space, a circumstance which gave Newton considerable food for thought (pail-experiment).[2]

Classical mechanics is only a general scheme; it becomes a theory only by explicit indication of the force laws (*d*) as was done so very successfully by Newton for celestial mechanics. From the point of view of the aim of the greatest logical simplicity of the foundations, this theoretical method is deficient in so far as the laws of force cannot be obtained by logical and formal considerations, so that their choice is *a priori* to a large extent arbitrary. Also Newton's gravitation law of force is distinguished from other conceivable laws of force exclusively by its *success*.

In spite of the fact that, today, we know positively that classical mechanics fails as a foundation dominating all physics, it still occupies the center of all of our thinking in physics. The reason for this lies in the fact that, regardless of important progress reached since the time of Newton, we have not yet arrived at a new foundation of physics concerning which we may be certain that the whole complexity of investigated phenomena, and of partial theoretical systems of a successful kind, could be deduced logically from it. In the

[2] This defect of the theory could only be eliminated by such a formulation of mechanics as would command validity for all B_0. This is one of the steps which lead to the general theory of relativity. A second defect, also eliminated only by the introduction of the general theory of relativity, lies in the fact that there is no reason given by mechanics itself for the equality of the gravitational and inertial mass of the material point.

following lines I shall try to describe briefly how the matter stands.

First we try to get clearly in our minds how far the system of classical mechanics has shown itself adequate to serve as a basis for the whole of physics. Since we are dealing here only with the foundations of physics and with its development, we need not concern ourselves with the purely *formal* progresses of mechanics (equation of Lagrange, canonical equations, etc.). *One* remark, however, appears indispensable. The notion "material point" is fundamental for mechanics. If now we seek the mechanics of a bodily object which itself can *not* be treated as a material point—and strictly speaking every object "perceptible to our senses" is of this category—then the question arises: How shall we imagine the object to be built up out of material points, and what forces must we assume as acting between them? The formulation of this question is indispensable, if mechanics is to pretend to describe the object *completely*.

It is natural to the tendency of mechanics to assume these material points, and the laws of forces acting between them, as invariable, since time alterations would lie outside of the scope of mechanical explanation. From this we can see that classical mechanics must lead us to an atomistic construction of matter. We now realize, with special clarity, how much in error are those theorists who believe that theory comes inductively from experience. Even the great Newton could not free himself from this error ("Hypotheses non fingo").*

In order to save itself from becoming hopelessly lost in this line of thought (atomistic), science proceeded first in the following manner. The mechanics of a system is determined if its potential energy is given as a function of its configuration. Now, if the acting forces are of such a kind as to guarantee maintenance of certain qualities of order of the system's configuration, then the configuration may be described with sufficient accuracy by a relatively small number of configuration variables q_r; the potential energy is considered only insofar as it is dependent upon *these* variables (for instance, description of the configuration of a practically rigid body by six variables).

A second method of application of mechanics, which avoids

* "I make no hypotheses."

the consideration of a subdivision of matter down to "real" material points, is the mechanics of so-called continuous media. This mechanics is characterized by the fiction that the density of matter and speed of matter is dependent in a continuous manner upon coordinates and time, and that the part of the interactions not explicitly given can be considered as surface forces (pressure forces) which again are continuous functions of location. Herein we find the hydrodynamic theory, and the theory of elasticity of solid bodies. These theories avoid the explicit introduction of material points by fictions which, in the light of the foundation of classical mechanics, can only have an approximate significance.

In addition to their great *practical* significance, these categories of science have—by enlargement of the mathematical world of ideas—created those formal auxiliary instruments (partial differential equations) which have been necessary for the subsequent attempts at formulating the total scheme of physics in a manner which is new as compared with that of Newton.

These two modes of application of mechanics belong to the so-called "phenomenological" physics. It is characteristic of this kind of physics that it makes as much use as possible of concepts which are close to experience but which, for this reason, have to give up to a large degree, unity in the foundations. Heat, electricity and light are described by special variables of state and constants of matter other than the mechanical state; and to determine all of these variables in their relative dependence was a rather empirical task. Many contemporaries of Maxwell saw in such a manner of presentation the ultimate aim of physics, which they thought could be obtained purely inductively from experience on account of the relative closeness of the concepts used to the experience. From the point of view of theories of knowledge St. Mill and E. Mach took their stand approximately on this ground.

According to my belief, the greatest achievement of Newton's mechanics lies in the fact that its consistent application has led beyond this phenomenological representation, particularly in the field of heat phenomena. This occurred in the kinetic theory of gases and, in a general way, in statistical mechanics. The former connected the equation of state of the ideal gases, viscosity, diffusion and heat conductivity of gases and radiometric phenomena of gases, and gave the logical connection of phenomena which, from the point of view of direct experience, had nothing whatever to do with one another. The latter gave a mechanical interpretation of the thermodynamic ideas and laws as well as the discovery of the limit of applicability of the notions and laws to the classical theory of heat. This kinetic theory which surpassed, by far, the phenomenological physics as regards the logical unity of its foundations, produced moreover definite values for the true magnitudes of atoms and molecules which resulted from several independent methods and were thus placed beyond the realm of reasonable doubt. These decisive progresses were paid for by the coordination of atomistic entities to the material points, the constructively speculative character of which entities being obvious. Nobody could hope ever to "perceive directly" an atom. Laws concerning variables connected more directly with experimental facts (for example: temperature, pressure, speed) were deduced from the fundamental ideas by means of complicated calculations. In this manner physics (at least part of it), originally more phenomenologically constructed, was reduced, by being founded upon Newton's mechanics for atoms and molecules, to a basis further removed from direct experiment, but more uniform in character.

§ 3. THE FIELD CONCEPT

In explaining optical and electrical phenomena Newton's mechanics has been far less successful than it has been in the fields cited above. It is true that Newton tried to reduce light to the motion of material points in his corpuscular theory of light. Later on, however, as the phenomena of polarization, diffraction and interference of light forced upon his theory more and more unnatural modifications, Huyghens' undulatory theory of light prevailed. Probably this theory owes its origin essentially to the phenomena of crystallographic optics and to the theory of sound, which was then already elaborated to a certain degree. It must be admitted that Huyghens' theory also was based in the first instance upon classical mechanics; but, the all-penetrating ether had to be assumed as the carrier of the waves and the structure of the ether, formed from material points, could not be explained by any known phenomenon. One could never get a clear picture of the interior forces governing the ether, nor of the forces acting between the ether and the "ponderable" matter. The foundations of this theory remained, therefore, eternally in the dark. The true basis was a partial differential equation, the reduction of which to mechanical elements remained always problematic.

For the theoretical conception of electric and magnetic phenomena one introduced, again, masses of a special kind, and between these masses one assumed the existence of forces acting at a distance, similar to Newton's gravitational forces. This special kind of matter, however, appeared to be lacking in the fundamental property of inertia; and, the forces acting between these masses and the ponderable matter remained obscure. To these difficulties there had to be added the polar character of these kinds of matter which did not fit into the scheme of classical mechanics. The basis of the theory became still more unsatisfactory when electrodynamic phenomena became known, notwithstanding the fact that these phenomena brought the physicist to the explanation of magnetic phenomena through electrodynamic phenomena and, in this way, made the assumption of magnetic masses superfluous. This progress had, indeed, to be paid for by increasing the complexity of the forces of interaction which had to be assumed as existing between electrical masses in motion.

The escape from this unsatisfactory situation by the electric field theory of Faraday and Maxwell represents probably the most profound transformation which has been experienced by the foundations of physics since Newton's time. Again, it has been a step in the direction of constructive speculation which has increased the distance between the foundation of the theory and what can be experienced by means of our five senses. The existence of the field manifests itself, indeed, only when electrically charged bodies are introduced into it. The differential equations of Maxwell connect the spacial and temporal differential coefficients of the electric and magnetic fields. The electric masses are nothing more than places of non-disappearing divergency of the electric field. Light waves appear as undulatory electromagnetic field processes in space.

To be sure, Maxwell still tried to interpret his field theory mechanically by means of mechanical ether models. But these attempts receded gradually to the background following the representation—purged of any unnecessary additions —by Heinrich Hertz, so that, in this theory the field finally took the fundamental position which had been occupied in Newton's mechanics by the material points. At first, however, this applied only for electromagnetic fields in empty space.

In its initial stage the theory was yet quite unsatisfactory for the interior of matter, because there, two electric vectors had to be introduced, which were connected by relations dependent on the nature of the medium, these relations being inaccessible to any theoretical analysis. An analogous situation arose in connection with the magnetic field, as well as in the relation between electric current density and the field.

Here H. A. Lorentz found an escape which showed, at the same time, the way to an electrodynamic theory of bodies in motion, a theory which was more or less free of arbitrary assumption. His theory was built on the following fundamental hypothesis:

Everywhere (including the interior of ponderable bodies) the seat of the field is the empty space. The participation of matter in electromagnetic phenomena has its origin only in the fact that the elementary particles of matter carry unalterable electric charges, and, on this account are subject on the one hand to the actions of ponderomotive forces and on the other hand possess the property of generating a field. The elementary particles obey Newton's law of motion for the material point.

This is the basis on which H. A. Lorentz obtained his synthesis of Newton's mechanics and Maxwell's field theory. The weakness of this theory lies in the fact that it tried to determine the phenomena by a combination of partial differential equations (Maxwell's field equations for empty space) and total differential equations (equations of motion of points), which procedure was obviously unnatural. The unsatisfactory part of the theory showed up externally by the necessity of assuming finite dimensions for the particles in order to prevent the electromagnetic field existing at their surfaces from becoming infinitely great. The theory failed moreover to give any explanation concerning the tremendous forces which hold the electric charges on the individual particles. H. A. Lorentz accepted these weaknesses of his theory, which were well known to him, in order to explain the phenomena correctly at least as regards their general lines.

Furthermore, there was one consideration which reached beyond the frame of Lorentz's theory. In the environment of an electrically charged body there is a magnetic field which furnishes an (apparent) contribution to its inertia. Should it not be possible to explain the *total* inertia of the particles electromagnetically? It is clear that this problem could be worked out satisfactorily only if the particles could be interpreted as regular solutions of the electromagnetic partial differential equations. The Maxwell equations in their original form do not, however, allow such a description of particles, because their corresponding solutions contain a singularity. Theoretical physicists have tried for a long time, therefore, to reach the goal by a modification of Maxwell's equations. These attempts have, however, not been crowned with success. Thus it happened that the goal of erecting a pure electromagnetic field theory of matter remained unattained for the time being, although in principle no objection could be raised against the possibility of reaching such a goal. The thing which deterred one in any further attempt in this direction was the lack of any systematic method leading to the solution. What appears certain to me, however, is that, in the foundations of any consistent field theory, there shall not be, in addition to the concept of field, any concept concerning particles. The whole theory must be based solely on partial differential equations and their singularity-free solutions.

§ 4. THE THEORY OF RELATIVITY

There is no inductive method which could lead to the fundamental concepts of physics. Failure to understand this fact constituted the basic philosophical error of so many investigators of the nineteenth century. It was probably the reason why the molecular theory, and Maxwell's theory were able to establish themselves only at a relatively late date. Logical thinking is necessarily deductive; it is based upon hypothetical concepts and axioms. How can we hope to choose the latter in such a manner as to justify us in expecting success as a consequence?

The most satisfactory situation is evidently to be found in cases where the new fundamental hypotheses are suggested by the world of experience itself. The hypothesis of the non-existence of perpetual motion as a basis for thermodynamics affords such an example of a fundamental hypothesis suggested by experience; the same thing holds for the principle of inertia of Galileo. In the same category, moreover, we find the fundamental hypotheses of the theory of relativity, which theory has led to an unexpected expansion and broadening of the field theory, and to the superseding of the foundations of classical mechanics.

The successes of the Maxwell-Lorentz theory have given great confidence in the validity of the electromagnetic equations for empty space and hence, in particular, to the statement that light travels "in space" with a certain constant speed c. Is this law of the invariablity of light velocity in relation to any desired inertial system valid? If it were not, then one specific inertial system or more accurately, one specific state of motion (of a body of reference), would be distinguished from all others. In opposition to this idea, however, stand all the mechanical and electromagnetic-optical facts of our experience.

For these reasons it was necessary to raise to the degree of a principle, the validity of the law of constancy of light velocity for all inertial systems. From this, it follows that the spacial coordinates X_1, X_2, X_3, and the time X_4, must be transformed according to the "Lorentz-transformation" which is characterized by invariance of the expression

$$ds^2 = dx_1{}^2 + dx_2{}^2 + dx_3{}^2 - dx_4{}^2$$

(if the unit of time is chosen in such a manner that the speed of light $c = 1$).

By this procedure time lost its absolute character, and was included with the "spacial" coordinates as of algebraically (nearly) similar character. The absolute character of time and particularly of simultaneity were destroyed, and the four dimensional description became introduced as the only adequate one.

In order to account, also, for the equivalence of all inertial systems with regard to all the phenomena of nature, it is necessary to postulate invariance of all systems of physical equations which express general laws, with regard to the Lorentzian transformation. The elaboration of this requirement forms the content of the special theory of relativity.

This theory is compatible with the equation of Maxwell; but, it is incompatible with the basis of classical mechanics. It is true that the equations of motion of the material point can be modified (and with them the expressions for momentum and kinetic energy of the material point) in such a manner as to satisfy the theory; but, the concept of the force of interaction, and with it the concept of potential energy of a system, lose their basis, because these concepts rest upon the idea of absolute instantaneousness. The field, as determined by differential equations, takes the place of the force.

Since the foregoing theory allows interaction only by fields, it requires a field theory of gravitation. Indeed, it is not difficult to formulate such a theory in which, as in Newton's theory, the gravitational fields can be reduced to a scalar which is the solution of a partial differential equation. However, the experimental facts expressed in Newton's theory of gravitation lead in another direction, that of the general theory of relativity.

Classical mechanics contains one point which is unsatisfactory in that, in the fundamentals, the same mass constant is met twice over in two different rôles, namely as "inertial mass" in the law of motion, and as "gravitational mass" in the law of gravitation. As a result of this, the acceleration of a body in a pure gravitational field is independent of its material; or, in a coordinate system of *uniform acceleration* (accelerated in relation to an "inertial system") the motions take place as they would in a homogeneous gravitational field (in relation to a "motionless" system of coordinates). If one assumes that the equivalence of these two cases is complete, then one attains an adaptation of our theoretical thinking to the fact that the gravitational and inertial masses are identical.

From this it follows that there is no longer any reason for favoring, as a fundamental principle, the "inertial systems"; and, we must admit as equivalent in their own right, also *non-linear* transformations of the coordinates (x_1, x_2, x_3, x_4). If we make such a transformation of a system of coordinates of the special theory of relativity, then the metric

$$ds^2 = dx_1{}^2 + dx_2{}^2 + dx_3{}^2 - dx_4{}^2$$

goes over to a general (Riemannian) metric of Bane

$$ds^2 = g_{\mu v}\, dx_\mu\ dx_v \quad \text{(Summed over } \mu \text{ and } v)$$

where the g , symmetrical in μ and v, are certain functions of $x_1 \ldots x_4$ which describe both the metric property, and the gravitational field in relation to the new system of coordinates.

The foregoing improvement in the interpretation of the mechanical basis must, however, be paid for in that—as becomes evident on closer scrutiny—the new coordinates could no longer be interpreted, as results of measurements by rigid bodies and clocks, as they could in the original system (an inertial system with vanishing gravitational field).

The passage to the general theory of relativity is realized by the assumption that such a representation of the field properties of space already mentioned, by functions $g_{\mu v}$ (that is to say by a Riemann metric), is also justified in the *general* case in which there is no system of coordinates in relation to which the metric takes the simple quasi-Euclidian form of the special theory of relativity.

Now the coordinates, by themselves, no longer express metric relations, but only the "neighborliness" of the things described, whose coordinates differ but little from one another. All transformations of the coordinates have to be admitted so long as these transformations are free from singularities. Only such equations as are covariant in relation to arbitrary transformations in this sense have meaning as expressions of general laws of nature (postulate of general covariancy).

The first aim of the general theory of relativity was a preliminary statement which, by giving up the requirement of constituting a closed thing in itself, could be connected in as simple a manner as possible with the "facts directly observed." Newton's gravitational theory gave an example, by restricting itself to the pure mechanics of gravitation. This preliminary statement may be characterized as follows:

(1) The concept of the material point and of its mass is retained. A law of motion is given for it, this law of motion being the translation of the law of inertia into the language

of the general theory of relativity. This law is a system of total differential equations, the system characteristic of the geodetic line.

(2) In place of Newton's law of interaction by gravitation, we shall find the system of the simplest generally covariant differential equations which can be set up for the $g_{\mu\nu}$-tensor. It is formed by equating to zero the once contracted Riemannian curvature tensor ($R\mu\nu = 0$).

This formulation permits the treatment of the problem of the planets. More accurately speaking, it allows the treatment of the problem of motion of material points of practically negligible mass in the gravitational field produced by a material point which itself is supposed to have no motion (central symmetry). It does not take into account the reaction of the "moved" material points on the gravitational field, nor does it consider how the central mass produces this gravitational field.

Analogy with classical mechanics shows that the following is a way to complete the theory. One sets up as field equation

$$R_{ik} - \tfrac{1}{2} g_{ik} R = - T_{ik}$$

where R represents the scalar of Riemannian curvature, T_{ik} the energy tensor of the matter in phenomenological representation. The left side of the equation is chosen in such a manner that its divergence disappears identically. The resulting disappearance of the divergence of the right side produces the "equations of motion" of matter, in the form of partial differential equations for the case where T_{ik} introduces, for the description of the matter, only *four* further functions independent of each other (for instance, density, pressure, and velocity components, where there is between the latter an identity, and between pressure and density an equation of condition).

By this formulation one reduces the whole mechanics of gravitation to the solution of a single system of covariant partial differential equations. The theory avoids all internal discrepancies which we have charged against the basis of classical mechanics. It is sufficient—as far as we know—for the representation of the observed facts of celestial mechanics. But, it is similar to a building, one wing of which is made of fine marble (left part of the equation), but the other wing of which is built of low grade wood (right side of equation). The phenomenological representation of matter is, in fact, only a crude substitute for a representation which would correspond to all known properties of matter.

There is no difficulty in connecting Maxwell's theory of the electromagnetic field with the theory of the gravitational field so long as one restricts himself to space, free of ponderable matter and free of electric density. All that is necessary is to put on the right hand side of the above equation for T_{ik}, the energy tensor of the electromagnetic field in empty space and to associate with the so modified system of equations the Maxwell field equation for empty space, written in general covariant form. Under these conditions there will exist, between all these equations, a sufficient number of the differential identities to guarantee their consistency. We may add that this necessary formal property of the total system of equations leaves arbitrary the choice of the sign of the member T_{ik}, a fact which was later shown to be important.

The desire to have, for the foundations of the theory, the greatest possible unity has resulted in several attempts to include the gravitational field and the electromagnetic field in one formal but homogeneous picture. Here we must mention particularly the five-dimensional theory of Kaluza and Klein. Having considered this possibility very carefully I feel that it is more desirable to accept the lack of internal uniformity of the original theory, because I do not consider that the totality of the hypothetical basis of the five-dimensional theory contains less of an arbitrary nature than does the original theory. The same statement may be made for the projective variety of the theory, which has been elaborated with great care, in particular, by v. Dantzig and by Pauli.

The foregoing considerations concern, exclusively, the theory of the field, free of matter. How are we to proceed from this point in order to obtain a complete theory of atomically constructed matter? In such a theory, singularities must certainly be excluded, since without such exclusion the differential equations do not completely determine the total field. Here, in the field theory of general relativity, we meet the same problem of a theoretical field-representation of matter as was met originally in connection with the pure Maxwell theory.

Here again the attempt to construct particles out of the

field theory, leads apparently to singularities. Here also the endeavor has been made to overcome this defect by the introduction of new field variables and by elaborating and extending the system of field equations. Recently, however, I discovered, in collaboration with Dr. Rosen, that the above mentioned simplest combination of the field equations of gravitation and electricity produces centrally symmetrical solutions which can be represented as free of singularity (the well known centrally symmetrical solutions of Schwarzschild for the pure gravational field, and those of Reissner for the electric field with consideration of its gravitational action). . . . In this way it seems possible to get for matter and its interactions a pure field theory free of additional hypotheses, one moreover whose test by submission to facts of experience does not result in difficulties other than purely mathematical ones, which difficulties, however, are very serious.

(d)

Einstein and the Idea of Freedom

I KNOW THAT IT IS a hopeless undertaking to debate about fundamental value judgments. For instance if someone approves, as a goal, the extirpation of the human race from the earth, one cannot refute such a viewpoint on rational grounds. But if there is agreement on certain goals and values, one can argue rationally about the means by which these objectives may be attained. Let us, then, indicate two goals which may well be agreed upon by nearly all who read these lines.

1. Those instrumental goods which should serve to maintain the life and health of all human beings should be produced by the least possible labor of all.

2. The satisfaction of physical needs is indeed the indispensable precondition of a satisfactory existence, but in itself it is not enough. In order to be content men must also have the possibility of developing their intellectual and artistic powers to whatever extent accord with their personal characteristics and abilities.

The first of these two goals requires the promotion of all knowledge relating to the laws of nature and the laws of social processes, that is, the promotion of all scientific endeavor. For scientific endeavor is a natural whole the parts of which mutually support one another in a way which, to be sure, no one can anticipate. However, the progress of science

Out of My Later Years, pp. 12-14.

presupposes the possibility of unrestricted communication of all results and judgments—freedom of expression and instruction in all realms of intellectual endeavor. By freedom I understand social conditions of such a kind that the expression of opinions and assertions about general and particular matters of knowledge will not involve dangers or serious disadvantages for him who expresses them. This freedom of communication is indispensable for the development and extension of scientific knowledge, a consideration of much practical import. In the first instance it must be guaranteed by law. But laws alone cannot secure freedom of expression; in order that every man may present his views without penalty there must be a spirit of tolerance in the entire population. Such an ideal of external liberty can never be fully attained but must be sought unremittingly if scientific thought, and philosophical and creative thinking in general, are to be advanced as far as possible.

If the second goal, that is, the possibility of the spiritual development of all individuals, is to be secured, a second kind of outward freedom is necessary. Man should not have to work for the achievement of the necessities of life to such an extent that he has neither time nor strength for personal activities. Without this second kind of outward liberty, freedom of expression is useless for him. Advances in technology would provide the possibility of this kind of freedom if the problem of a reasonable division of labor were solved.

The development of science and of the creative activities of the spirit in general requires still another kind of freedom, which may be characterized as inward freedom. It is this freedom of the spirit which consists in the independence of thought from the restrictions of authoritarian and social prejudices as well as from unphilosophical routinizing and habit in general. This inward freedom is an infrequent gift of nature and a worthy objective for the individual. Yet the community can do much to further this achievement, too, at least by not interfering with its development. Thus schools may interfere with the development of inward freedom through authoritarian influences and through imposing on young people excessive spiritual burdens; on the other hand schools may favor such freedom by encouraging independent thought. Only if outward and inner freedom are constantly and consciously pursued is there a possibility of spiritual development and perfection and thus of improving man's outward and inner life.

(e)

A Message to Intellectuals

WE MEET TODAY, as intellectuals and scholars of many nationalities, with a deep and historic responsibility placed upon us. We have every reason to be grateful to our French and Polish colleagues whose initiatives has assembled us here for a momentous objective: to use the influence of wise men in promoting peace and security throughout the world. This is the age-old problem with which Plato, as one of the first, struggled so hard: to apply reason and prudence to the solution of man's problems instead of yielding to atavist instincts and passions.

By painful experience we have learnt that rational thinking does not suffice to solve the problems of our social life. Penetrating research and keen scientific work have often had tragic implications for mankind, producing, on the one hand, inventions which liberated man from exhausting physical labor, making his life easier and richer; but on the other hand, introducing a grave restlessness into his life, making him a slave to his technological environment, and—most catastrophic of all—creating the means for his own mass destruction. This, indeed, is a tragedy of overwhelming poignancy!

This address was objected to by the Organizing Committee of the Intellectuals' Conference for Peace. The message was subsequently released to the press on August 29, 1948. Reprinted in *Out of My Later Years*, pp. 152-155.

However poignant that tragedy is, it is perhaps even more tragic that, while mankind has produced many scholars so extremely successful in the field of science and technology, we have been for a long time so inefficient in finding adequate solutions to the many political conflicts and economic tensions which beset us. No doubt, the antagonism of economic interests within and among nations is largely responsible to a great extent for the dangerous and threatening condition in the world today. Man has not succeeded in developing political and economic forms of organization which would guarantee the peaceful coexistence of the nations of the world. He has not succeeded in building the kind of system which would eliminate the possibility of war and banish forever the murderous instruments of mass destruction.

We scientists, whose tragic destination has been to help in making the methods of annihilation more gruesome and more effective, must consider it our solemn and transcendent duty to do all in our power in preventing these weapons from being used for the brutal purpose for which they were invented. What task could possibly be more important for us? What social aim could be closer to our hearts? That is why this Congress has such a vital mission. We are here to take counsel with each other. We must build spiritual and scientific bridges linking the nations of the world. We must overcome the horrible obstacles of national frontiers.

In the smaller entities of community life, man has made some progress toward breaking down anti-social sovereignties. This is true, for example, of life within cities and, to a certain degree, even of society within individual states. In such communities tradition and education have had a moderating influence and have brought about tolerable relations among the peoples living within those confines. But in relations among separate states complete anarchy still prevails. I do not believe that we have made any genuine advance in this area during the last few thousand years. All too frequently conflicts among nations are still being decided by brutal power, by war. The unlimited desire for ever greater power seeks to become active and aggressive wherever and whenever the physical possibility offers itself.

Throughout the ages, this state of anarchy in international affairs has inflicted indescribable suffering and destruction upon mankind; again and again it has depraved the development of men, their souls and their well-being. For given time it has almost annihilated whole areas.

However, the desire of nations to be constantly prepared for warfare has, however, still other repercussions upon the lives of men. The power of every state over its citizens has grown steadily during the last few hundred years, no less in countries where the power of the state has been exercised wisely, than in those where it has been used for brutal tyranny. The function of the state to maintain peaceful and ordered relations among and between its citizens has become increasingly complicated and extensive largely because of the concentration and centralization of the modern industrial apparatus. In order to protect its citizens from attacks from without a modern state requires a formidable, expanding military establishment. In addition, the state considers it necessary to educate its citizens for the possibilities of war, an "education" not only corrupting to the soul and spirit of the young, but also adversely affecting the mentality of adults. No country can avoid this corruption. It pervades the citizenry even in countries which do not harbor outspoken aggressive tendencies. The state has thus become a modern idol whose suggestive powers few men are able to escape.

Education for war, however, is a delusion. The technological developments of the last few years have created a completely new military situation. Horrible weapons have been invented, capable of destroying in a few seconds huge masses of human beings and tremendous areas of territory. Since science has not yet found protection from these weapons, the modern state is no longer in a position to prepare adequately for the safety of its citizens.

How, then, shall we be saved?

Mankind can only gain protection against the danger of unimaginable destruction and wanton annihilation if a supranational organization has alone the authority to produce or possess these weapons. It is unthinkable, however, that nations under existing conditions would hand over such authority to a supranational organization unless the organization would have the legal right and duty to solve all the conflicts which in the past have led to war. The functions of individual states would be to concentrate more or less upon internal affairs; in their relation with other states they would deal only with issues and problems which are in no way conducive to endangering international security.

Unfortunately, there are no indications that governments yet realize that the situation in which mankind finds itself makes the adoption of revolutionary measures a compelling necessity. Our situation is not comparable to anything in the past. It is impossible, therefore, to apply methods and measures which at an earlier age might have been sufficient. We must revolutionize our thinking, revolutionize our actions, and must have the courage to revolutionize relations among the nations of the world. Clichés of yesterday will no longer do today, and will, no doubt, be hopelessly out of date tomorrow. To bring this home to men all over the world is the most important and most fateful social function intellectuals have ever had to shoulder. Will they have enough courage to overcome their own national ties to the extent that is necessary to induce the people of the world to change their deep-rooted national traditions in a most radical fashion?

A tremendous effort is indepensable. If it fails now, the supranational organization will be built later, but then it will have to be built upon the ruins of a large part of the now existing world. Let us hope that the abolition of the existing international anarchy will not need to be bought by a self-inflicted world catastrophe the dimensions of which none of us can possibly imagine. The time is terribly short. We must act now if we are to act at all.

(f)

A Few of Albert Einstein's Opinions

WHEN ASKED ABOUT the minimum knowledge every student should possess, Einstein replied:

"I don't really know. Personally I never clutter up my memory with facts I can easily find in an encyclopedia."

On another occasion, he added: "One should never cram young minds with facts, names and formulae. To know them you have no need of university courses, you can find them in books. Education should only be used to teach young people to think and to give them this training which no textbooks can replace. It is really miraculous that modern education has not completely suffocated the sacred curiosity of research. I believe that one could even cure a wild beast of its voracity if, under the threat of the whip, it was constantly made to eat when it was not hungry and above all if one selected the food one forced it to swallow."

People sometimes tried to embarrass Einstein by asking him questions about religion. On one occasion he replied:

"I believe in the god of Spinoza who reveals himself in a harmony of all creatures, and not in a god who busies himself with the fate and actions of men."

As far as certain inexplicable but sometimes disturbing phenomena were concerned, he was far removed from systematic negation.

"It is possible," he said, "that human emanations of which we are ignorant exist. Remember how people ridiculed the

161

existence of electric currents and invisible waves. Our knowledge of the human being is still in its infancy."

According to Antonina Vallentin he once confessed: "I am inclined to believe in telepathy, but it probably has more to do with physics than with psychology."

Sommerfeld asked him one day: "Do you believe that any reality exists outside ourselves?"

"Yes, I believe it," Einstein replied.

But this by no means implied the idea of an anthropomorphic god such as the religions—and above all the churches—try to present to man. He wrote:*

"The more a man is imbued with the ordered regularity of all events the firmer becomes his conviction that there is no room left by the side of this ordered regularity for causes of a different nature. For him neither the rule of human nor the rule of divine will exists as an independent cause of natural events. To be sure, the doctrine of a personal God interfering with natural events could never be *refuted,* in the real sense, by science, for this doctrine can always take refuge in those domains in which scientific knowledge has not yet been able to set foot.

"But I am persuaded that such behavior on the part of the representatives of religion would not only be unworthy but also fatal. For a doctrine which is able to maintain itself not in clear light but only in the dark, will of necessity lose its effect on mankind, with incalculable harm to human progress."

He did however add:

"If it is one of the goals of religion to liberate mankind as far as possible from the bondage of egocentric cravings, desires, and fears, scientific reasoning can aid religion in yet another sense. Although it is true that it is the goal of science to discover rules which permit the association and foretelling of facts, this is not its only aim. It also seeks to reduce the connections discovered to the smallest possible number of mutually independent conceptual elements. It is in this striving after the rational unification of the manifold that it encounters its greatest successes, even though it is precisely this attempt which causes it to run the greatest risk of falling a prey to illusions. But whoever has undergone the intense experience of successful advances made in this domain, is

* In "Science and Religion," *Out of My Later Years.*

moved by profound reverence for the rationality made manifest in existence. By way of the understanding he achieves a far-reaching emancipation from the shackles of personal hopes and desires, and thereby attains that humble attitude of mind towards the grandeur of reason incarnate in existence, and which, in its profoundest depths, is inaccessible to man. This attitude, however, appears to me to be religious, in the highest sense of the word. And so it seems to me that science not only purifies the religious impulse of the dross of its anthropomorphism but also contributes to a religious spiritualization of our understanding of life.

"The further the spiritual evolution of mankind advances, the more certain it seems to me that the path to genuine religiosity does not lie through the fear of life, and the fear of death, and blind faith, but through striving after rational knowledge."

We must not fail to take into account this particular concept of religiosity when Einstein uses the word 'religion'. He had nothing of the cold contemplative, content to express physical phenomena in formulae, but on the contrary in common with every mind which has only once seriously and deeply asked this question to which there is no answer: "Why does the world exist? Why does life exist, and why have I a knowledge of existing?" he was seized with a kind of mystic exaltation at the thought of these mysteries and marveled at the strange harmony of the world which was demonstrable mathematically.

"The finest emotion of which we are capable," he wrote, "is the mystic emotion. Herein lies the germ of all art and all true science. Anyone to whom this feeling is alien, who is no longer capable of wonderment and lives in a state of fear is a dead man. To know that what is impenetrable for us really exists and manifests itself as the highest wisdom and the most radiant beauty, whose gross forms alone are intelligible to our poor faculties,—this knowledge, this feeling . . . that is the core of the true religious sentiment. In this sense and in this sense alone, I rank myself among profoundly religious men."

This is what he called his "cosmic religion" of which he said:*

* In *Cosmic Religion* (New York: Covici-Friede, 1931), pp. 52-53.

". . . the cosmic religious experience is the strongest and the noblest driving force behind scientific research. No one who does not appreciate the terrific exertions, and, above all, the devotion without which pioneer creations in scientific thought cannot come into being, can judge the strength of the feeling out of which alone such work, turned away as it is from immediate practical life, can grow. What a deep faith in the rationality of the structure of the world and what a longing to understand even a small glimpse of the reason revealed in the world there must have been in Kepler and Newton. . . ."

GLOSSARY OF SCIENTIFIC TERMS

ÁNGSTRÖM: Unit of length used in microphysics, equal to one ten millionth of a millimeter.

ATOM: The smallest particle of an element capable of combining. Contrary to its etymology it is not indivisible but must be considered as a dynamic system, i.e. whose components, nuclei and electrons (cf. infra) are in perpetual movement.

CATALYST: A substance which, without undergoing visible transformation, provokes or accelerates a reaction (chemical or nuclear).

COORDINATES: Elements serving to determine the position of a point on an area or in space (and in relativity, in time) in relation to a system of reference.

COSMOS: The universe considered as a whole: macrocosm on the large and microcosm on the small scale.

ELECTRON: Particle of small mass with a diameter of the order of 1 billionth of a millimeter and bearing an electric charge: a flow of electrons causes the electric effect. In the atom, the electron charged with electricity (with the negative sign) revolves schematically round the nucleus. There are an equal number of electrons and protons to keep the balance of electric charges: the atom as a whole in its normal state being neutral from the electric point of view.

ENERGY: In the cosmic sense the effect of a cause which eludes us completely.

165

EVENT: In the sense it is employed in this book, and referring to relativity, any cosmic phenomenon considered.

FREQUENCY: The number of periods per second of vibratory motion.

KINEMATICS: The branch of mechanics which studies the movements of bodies apart from the forces which produce them.

KINETICS: Relative to movement; kinetic energy is the energy of a body in motion; for a solid in movement of translation it is half the product of its mass and the square of its velocity.

MESON: An unstable particle materializing in the nuclear field. There are several aspects of mesons. Their mass varies between approximately 207 times the mass of the electron to 966 times this mass (heavy mesons).

NEUTRON: Heavy particle (1837 times the mass of an electron) unstable in its free state, preexisting in the nucleus of atoms (apart from the hydrogen nucleus which is formed of a single proton). Neutral from the electric point of view, it has just been proved that the neutron actually bears a positive and a negative charge which cancel out.

NUCLEON: The proton or the neutron irrespectively.

PROTON: Heavy particle (1835 times the mass of the electron). Basic particle of the atom nucleus charged with electricity (positive).
The nucleus of the hydrogen atom is the proton of all atoms.

HALF-LIFE PERIOD: In nuclear physics the time at the end of which the activity of a radio-element diminishes by half its value or alternatively the time at the end of which half the mass of this element will be transmuted. A radioactive element having a period of 20 years will see its mass diminish by half at the end of 20 years: of a gram there will remain half a gram and of this half gram a quarter gram at the end of a new period of 20 years, etc. The rest will be transformed into lighter elements.

PHOTON: Stable particle with a rest mass of zero materializing in the electromagnetic field. The photon is the "speck" of light.

POSTULATE: Mathematical property admitted without demonstration.

STATISTICS: Scientific method consisting in grouping and observing the reactions of a certain number of collective facts whose nature and the inadequacy of the means of investigation prevent separate explanation, and of producing laws justifiably called "statistical". Thus the study of atomic, nuclear and subnuclear events (cf. supra) can only be done today "statistically", just as it is only statistically that we can try to enumerate for example the constituent particles of the universe, (the results would only be of value if we could be certain that the universe were limited in space and time).

BIBLIOGRAPHY

WORKS BY EINSTEIN

Sidelights on Relativity, trans. G. B. Jeffery and W. Perret (New York: E. P. Dutton, 1922).

About Zionism: Speeches and Letters, trans. and ed. by L. Simon (New York: Macmillan Co., 1931).

The World as I See It, trans. A. Harris (New York: The Philosophical Library, 1949).

Out of My Later Years (New York: The Philosophical Library, 1950).

Relativity: The Special and the General Theory, trans. R. W. Lawson (New York: Holt, 1920).

The Meaning of Relativity, trans. E. P. Adams (Princeton, N. J.: Princeton Univ. Press, 1923).

Investigations on the Theory of the Brownian Movement, ed. R. Fürth, trans. A. D. Cowper (New York: Dover Publications, 1965).

Why War? "Open Letters" between Einstein and Freud (World Peace Foundation 1933).

Ideas and Opinions by Albert Einstein, based on *Mein Weltbild,* ed. C. Seelig, and Other Sources; new trans. and rev. by S. Bargmann (New York: Crown Publishers, 1954).

Einstein on Peace, ed. O. Nathan and H. Norden (New York: Simon and Schuster, 1960).

169

The Evolution of Physics, with Leopold Infeld (New York: Simon and Schuster, 1954).

WORKS ON EINSTEIN

L. Barnett, *The Universe and Dr. Einstein* (New York: William Sloane Associates, 1948).

A. Beckhard, *Albert Einstein* (New York: G. P. Putnam's Sons, 1959).

A. C. Bill, *An Englishwoman's Reply to Einstein* (New York: A. A. Beauchamp, 1930).

H. Bondi, *Relativity and Common Sense* (New York: Doubleday, 1964).

M. Born, *Einstein's Theory of Relativity,* trans. H. H. L. A. Brose (New York: E. P. Dutton, 1924).

W. Cahn, *Einstein: A Pictorial Biography* (New York: Citadel Press, 1955).

E. Cassirer, *Substance and Function, and Einstein's Theory of Relativity,* trans. W. G. S. and M. C. Swabey (Chicago: Open Court Publishing Co., 1923 and New York: Dover Publications, 1953).

A. Forsee, *Albert Einstein: Theoretical Physicist* (New York: Macmillan Co., 1963).

P. Franck, *Einstein: His Life and Times* (New York: Alfred A. Knopf, 1948).

H. G. Garbedian, *Albert Einstein, Maker of Universes* (New York: Funk & Wagnalls Co., 1939).

S. H. Guggenheimer, *The Einstein Theory Explained and Analyzed* (New York: Macmillan Co., 1925).

B. Harrow, *From Newton to Einstein* (Princeton, N. J.: Van Nostrand Co., 1920).

L. Infeld, *Albert Einstein, His Work and Its Influence on Our World* (New York Charles Scribner's Sons, 1950).

L. D. Landau and G. Rumer, *What is Relativity?,* trans. N. Kemmer (New York: Premier Books, 1966).

E. E. Levinger, *Albert Einstein* (New York: Julian Messner, 1949).

A. A. Lynch, *The Case Against Einstein* (London: Philip Allan, 1932 and New York: Dodd, 1933).

D. J. MacAdam, *Einstein's Relativity: A Criticism* (Boston: R. G. Badger, 1922).

D. Marianoff, and P. Wayne, *Einstein* (New York: Doubleday, 1944).

P. MICHELMORE, *Einstein, Profile of the Man* (New York: Dodd, 1962).

A. MOSZKOWSKI, *Einstein the Searcher,* trans. H. H. L. A. Brose (New York: E. P. Dutton, 1922).

G. NORDMANN, *Einstein and the Universe,* trans. J. MacCabe (New York: Henry Holt, 1922).

T. P. NUNN, *Relativity and Gravitation* (New York: E. P. Dutton, 1923).

L. PAGE, *The Principle of General Relativity and Einstein's Theory of Gravitation* [In: *Trans. of Conn. Acad. of Sci. and Arts,* Vol. 23] (New Haven: Yale Univ. Press, 1920).

M. PALMIERI, *Relativity* (Los Angeles: Forbush Publishing Co., 1931).

C. O. PEARCE, *Albert Einstein: A Biography for Young People* (New York: Henry Holt, 1949).

ALBERT EINSTEIN [AND OTHERS], *Living Philosophies* (New York: Simon and Schuster, 1931).

C. L. POOR, *Gravitation Versus Relativity* (New York: G. P. Putnam's Sons, 1922).

A. REISER, *Albert Einstein.* A Biographical Portrait (New York: Boni, 1930).

P. A. SCHILPP (Editor), *Albert Einstein: Philosopher-Scientist.* Vol. 7: (New York: The Library of Living Philosophers, 1949).

P. A. SCHILPP (Editor), *Albert Einstein: Philosopher-Scientist.* The Library of Living Philosophers (Second Edition) (New York: Tudor Publishing Co., 1951).

M. SCHLICK, *Space and Time in Contemporary Physics* (New York: Oxford University Press, 1920).

H. SCHMIDT, *Relativity and the Universe,* trans. K. Wichmann (New York: McBride, 1922).

G. P. SERVISS, *Einstein Theory of Relativity* (New York: E. M. Fadman, Inc., 1923).

H. H. SHELDON, *Space, Time, and Relativity* (New York: University Society, 1932).

E. E. SLOSSON, *Easy Lessons in Einstein* (New York: Harcourt, 1920).

J. H. THIRRING, *The Ideas of Einstein's Theory,* trans. R. A. B. Russell (New York: McBride, 1921).

A. VALLENTIN, *Einstein: A Biography,* trans. from the French by M. Budberg (New York: Doubleday, 1954).

W. WISE, *Albert Einstein, Citizen of the World* (New York: Farrar, Straus, 1960).

INDEX

Aarau, 19
acceleration, 26-27, 32, 54, 56, 71, 73-74, 147
admiration, 115
Albert, King of the Belgians, 97
anarchy, international, 157-160
ångström, 165
antineutrons, 55-57
antiprotons, 55-57
anti-Semitism, 19, 64, 94-95
atomic bomb, 100-104, 105
atoms, 22, 26, 31, 52, 84, 165

Barnett, Lincoln, 37, 38
Bavarian Academy of Science, 98
Becquerel, Antoine Henri, 52, 100
Bergson, Henri, 44
Berlin, 64-67, 94-97
Berne, 20, 64
Bohr, Niels, 60, 101
Bolyai, Farkas, 81
Born, Max, 69-70
Broglie, Louis de, 35, 92
Brown, Robert, 21
Brownian movement, 20, 21

capitalism, 106-108
Caputh (Berlin), 95, 97
catalyst, 165
Centre Européen de Recherches Nucléaires (C.E.R.N.), 54, 57
Chaplin, Charlie, 12
"clocks, slowing down of", 44-47, 76, 78, 84
comprehensibility, 131
constellations, 25, 36, 39-40, 45
contact, 135-136
contraction of measuring rods, 34-35, 40-44, 46
convictions, 120
coordinates, 27, 30, 33, 36-38, 43, 46, 62, 76, 77-79, 147, 165
cosmic religion, 163-164
cosmos, 25, 165
Couderc, Paul, 43
Curie, Marie, 52, 99, 100-101
Curie, Pierre, 52, 100-101

democracy, 121
Descartes, 30, 136
discipline, 16, 18
discontinuity, 24
Doppler effect, 48, 84

172

eclipse (1919), 83
Eddington, Sir Arthur, 31
education, 158, 161
Einstein, Elsa (second wife), 65, 67, 95, 96, 97, 99, 109
Einstein, Hermann (father), 14-15, 18, 19
Einstein, Maya (sister), 14
Einstein, Mileva (first wife), 20, 64, 109
electromagnetic field, 23, 26, 56, 60, 91, 143-145, 150
electrons, 22, 26, 55, 165
Elizabeth, Queen of the Belgians, 97
emulation, 108
energy, 165; equal to mass, 26, 50, 52
energy-mass, increase of, 50-57
ether, 28, 69
ethics, 125-127
Euclidean geometry, 27, 30, 77, 79, 137
events, 31, 33-34, 166

Faraday, Sir Michael, 75, 143
Fermi, Enrico, 101, 103
fetishism, 124
field concept of, 142-145
five-dimensional theory, 150
Fizeau, A. H. L., 51
force, 138-139
four-dimensional idea, 78-79, 146
"frame of reference," 33, 35, 146
Franck, Professor Philipp, 13, 15, 59, 60, 66-67
freedom, 153-155
frequency, 166
Fresnel, Augustin, 23

Galileo, 27, 32, 50, 71, 75-77
Gauss, Karl Friedrich, 59, 77, 81
Geneva, 54, 57
geodesics, 81

geometry, 27, 29, 77, 80-81, 136-137
gods, 125
gravitational field, 60, 71-75, 77, 86-87, 147, 149, 150, 151

Haber, Fritz, 95
Hahn, Otto, 101
half-life period, 166
Handford reactors, 103
Heisenberg, Werner, 101
Helmholtz, H. L. F., 59
Hertz, Henri, 59, 144
Hollitscher, Walter, 61
Hume, David, 59
Huyghens, Christian, 23, 142
hyperons, 57

imagination, 123
impulses, 123
individual, the, 105, 126-127
inertia, 26, 32, 36, 50, 54, 71, 72-75, 138, 139, 146-149
Infeld, Leopold, 59
instincts, primary, 123, 124
intelligence, 120
international anarchy, 157-160
isolationism, 109, 117
Ives, H. E., 51

Jeans, Sir James, 88
Joliot-Curie, Frédéric, 101, 102
Joliot-Curie, Irene, 101
Jungk, Robert, 103

Kaluza, 150
Kant, Immanuel, 29, 44, 45, 59, 131
kinematics, 30, 75, 166
kinetics, 54, 141, 166
Kirchhoff, Gustav, 59
Klein, Felix, 150
Kowarski, 102

Langevin, Paul, 30, 49, 99
language, 17
Le Coq (Belgium), 99

Lemaitre, Georges, 90
Lenard, Philipp, 23
Lenin, 105
Leverrier, U. J. J., 87
life, as a "becoming," 116
light, 22-24 and *passim*
light, speed of, 26, 35, 62-63;
    constancy of, 28-29, 32, 34,
    37, 48-50, 51-52, 81-84, 146;
    and increase of energy-mass,
    50-57
Lobatchevski, Nikolai, 77, 81
Lorentz, H. A., 34-36, 59, 144-
    147
Lorentz transformation, 35, 37-
    38, 42, 48, 51, 79, 144-147

Mach, Ernst, 59, 60, 141
man, in society, 105-106
"Manhattan Project," 102
Mann, Heinrich, 94
Marianoff, Margot (daughter),
    109
mass, equal to energy, 26, 50, 52
material point, 138, 140, 147,
    148
materialism, 60, 61
mathematics, 16-18, 119
matter, creation of, 55-57
Maxwell, James Clerk, 23, 59,
    75, 141, 143-147, 150
meaning, 130-131
measurement, true, 43
measuring rods, contraction of,
    40-44, 46, 78
mechanics, 134-142; applied,
    141; classical, 29, 37, 79, 85-
    86, 138-140, 142-143, 147,
    149
Meitner, Lise, 101
Mercury, 87
mesons, 23-24, 49-50, 51, 166
Michelson, Albert, 28, 34, 41,
    52
Milan, 19
militarism, 16, 18, 117, 159
Miller, Dayton Clarence, 52
Minkowsky, Hermann, 78, 79
molecules, 21

money, 12
monotheism, 126
Monzie, Anatole de, 99, 100
moral imperative, 116, 124-127
Morley, E. W., 28, 34, 41, 52
movement, 31-34, 36-38, 70 *et
    seq.*
Munich, 14-19
music, 16, 18
mysticism, 163

Nernst, Walter, 64
neutrons, 55-56, 166
Newton, Sir Isaac, 23, 29, 32,
    44, 50, 71, 72, 87, 139, 140,
    141, 142, 143
Nietzsche, Friedrich, 59
non-acceleration, 32
nuclear energy, 53, 55-57, 100-
    104
nucleon, 166

pacifism, 100, 118-119
Painlevé, Paul, 99
Pauli, Wolfgang, 150
Peace Congress of Intellectuals
    (1948), 157-160
phenomenological physics, 141-
    142
philosophy, 59-60, 129
photons, 23, 166
physics, and reality, 129-145
Planck, Max, 20, 22, 60, 64
planets, 27, 29, 75, 86-88
Poincaré, Henri, 59, 134
political freedom, 97
positivism, 60
postulate, 167
Prague, 64
Princeton University, 95, 99,
    109
principles, 124-127
protons, 53, 55-57, 166
Prout, William, 52
Prussian Academy of Science,
    64, 65, 98

quantum, theory, 20, 22, 23, 91,
    92, 151

radiation, 22-23, 54, 84
radioactivity, 52, 100
Rathenau, Walter, 95
reality, 24, 26, 43, 59, 60, 80, 81, 119, 162; and physics, 129-151
relativity, 59, 60-63, 137-138, 145-151; general theory of, 69-73, 139, 147, 148-151; special theory of, 20, 24-29, 69-70, 71, 76, 77, 85, 147
religion, 15, 19, 94, 120-121, 125-126, 161-164
Riemann, G. F. B., 59, 77, 81, 148, 149
rockets, 48-49, 50-51
rods, contraction of, 40-44, 46, 78
Rolland, Romain, 65
Roosevelt, Franklin D. , 100, 101, 103
Rosen, Dr, 151
Rutherford, Lord, 101

Schopenhauer, Arthur, 59
Schrödinger, Erwin, 92
scientific method, 129-134; stratification of, 132-134
simultaneity, 27, 35, 39-41, 61-62, 138
Sitter, Willem de, 28
socialism, 118-119
society, 116, 126
solar system, 25, 32-33, 39, 62, 86-88
Sommerfeld, Arnold, 162
space, 29, 136-137, 139; and time, 27, 29-32, 34-36, 42-43, 48-50, 51
space-time continuum, 77-79, 85-88

specific gravity, 72, 77-78
speed, 48. See also light
stars, 24-25, 27, 29, 39, 45, 62, 75, 83
statistics, 167
synchrophasotrons, 54, 57
Szilard, Leo, 103

thermodynamics, 142, 146
thought, 124, 130-132
time, 44-48, 62; measurement of, 30-31; objective, 134, 137-138; subjective, 134
time and space, 27, 29-32, 34-36, 42-43
tolerance, 127
Tricentenary of High Education, 108

unified field theory, 24, 90-92
universe, Einstein's theory of, 88-90
University of California, 56, 57
uranium, 102

Vallentin, Antonina, 12, 14, 93, 98, 99, 110, 162
Vigier, Jean-Pierre, 92

world government, 105, 109

Young, Thomas, 23

Zionism, 94
Zürich, 19-20, 64, 78